**BREAKDOWN**
**A History of Recovε**

CW01020586

ISBN 0 11 290456 4

Front cover
Chieftain ARV winching a Chieftain hulk up a steep
slope on the SEME training area.

Back cover
Two Scammell Explorers of 10 Infantry Workshop
REME in Korea pulling a 50-ton Dyson trailer carrying
a Centurion tank. (Photo DJ Davies.)

# A History of

A 'crock train' towed by a Dodge WK 60 gantry lorry. All vehicles
in the train apart from the trailer are captured Italian or German
trucks.

REME MUSEUM
Royal Electrical and Mechanical Engineers

# BREAKDOWN

## Recovery Vehicles in the British Army

Brian S. Baxter

*London*   Her Majesty's Stationery Office

# Contents

Introduction   vi

Part 1   From Horse to Horsepower   1
*Chapter 1*   The Early Development of Mechanical Transport   2
*Chapter 2*   The First World War: Motor Transport and Tanks   3
*Chapter 3*   First World War Salvage Systems and Equipment   6

Part 2   Scrimp and Save: 1919 to 1939   9
*Chapter 1*   Changes in the War Office and the Army's Repair Organisations   10
*Chapter 2*   Equipment Design in the 1920s and 1930s.   12
*Chapter 3*   Recovery Vehicles in the Inter-War Period   15
*Chapter 4*   Tank Recovery and the First Tank Transporters   19

Part 3   The Second World War   23
*Chapter 1*   The Outbreak of War: The Campaign in France and Belgium and its Legacies   24
*Chapter 2*   1940–1941: The Campaigns in North and East Africa and Contemporary Equipment   27
*Chapter 3*   1941–1942: New Organisations and New Equipment   32
*Chapter 4*   1941–1943: The Continued War in the Middle East and North Africa   38
*Chapter 5*   1942–1944: Further Developments in the United Kingdom   41
*Chapter 6*   The Campaigns in Sicily and Italy   43
*Chapter 7*   1942–1945 Armoured Recovery Vehicles and New Transporters   47
*Chapter 8*   D Day and the North West Europe Campaign   54
*Chapter 9*   The War Against Japan: India and South East Asia   59

Part 4   The Development of Recovery Vehicles Since 1945   63
*Chapter 1*   The Post-War Situation: The 1940s and 1950s   64
*Chapter 2*   Recovery Vehicles and Transporters in the 1940s and 1950s   66
*Chapter 3*   The First Post-War ARVs   74
*Chapter 4*   The 1960s: New Philosophies and New Designs   81
*Chapter 5*   The 1970s and 1980s: Newer Armoured Recovery Vehicles   87
*Chapter 6*   Further Progress in Wheeled Recovery Vehicles and Transporters   91

Glossary of Abbreviations   97
Acknowledgements   98
Index   99

# Introduction

This book grew out of a series of articles written for the Royal Electrical and Mechanical Engineers (REME) *Journal*. REME has, since its formation in 1942, been the Army Corps mainly involved in vehicle recovery but it has always been an Army requirement that any driver of a military vehicle should cure simple faults and that the unit owning the vehicle should recover it if only a tow was needed: thus to an extent, recovery is of concern to all branches of the Army which operate vehicles.

This book describes the development of recovery vehicles against a background of contemporary technology, military campaigns, economics and numerous other influences.

REME inherited the recovery role from its principal forebear, the Engineering Branch of the Royal Army Ordnance Corps (RAOC(E)). Much expertise came also from the workshop personnel of the Royal Army Service Corps (RASC) which for many years had been the main operator of Army transport vehicles. The RASC's major workshops were incorporated into REME in 1942 but each transport company workshop remained RASC until 1951 when REME took over the remaining RASC repair facilities. The salvaging of disabled tanks began as a Tank Corps task but when, after World War I, the RAOC took over tank Corps workshops and began to provide each tank battalion with a Light Aid Detachment (LAD), tank recovery was practiced by both the RAOC and the battalion's own tradesmen. REME inherited the task from the RAOC and when, in 1951, its expanded LADs replaced Royal Armoured Corps (RAC) technical tradesmen REME assumed the main responsibility for tank recovery.

The word 'recovery' came into use in this context in the 1930s in the RAOC. It was used in the sense of 'bringing back' damaged equipment to a place of repair. In the early years of the century and during World War I the term mostly used was 'salvage'. Recovery may vary from the towing away of a vehicle broken down on a peacetime city street to the extrication from a ditch of a battle-damaged tank in wartime, while under enemy fire. Later, within the overall work of recovery, 'backloading' became the separately defined task of moving a concentration of vehicle casualties to a workshop further to the rear of the fighting line.

Many of the basic techniques of recovery and tools of the trade were developed in the period up to the nineteenth century for dragging guns into inaccessible places, thus winches, jacks, pulleys, shackles, anchors, gun planks and the shovel in one form or another have a history reaching much further back than the self-propelled vehicle. This knowledge and expertise was quickly adapted for use with traction engines from the 1860s.

This book is devoted to the means of recovery but it is proper to pay tribute, if only briefly, to the men upon whom this back-breaking work fell. They were from many regiments and corps before and even after REME was formed. Many were simply drivers and driver mechanics with recovery expertise acquired from arduous experience. In the RAOC, and in REME originally, the necessary skills were not deemed important enough to warrant a separate trade. In 1944 Fitters Motor Transport specialising in recovery became Fitters MT (recovery), sometimes FMRs, and after the war the trade became Recovery Mechanic. The work has always been the same, demanding men of resource with an independent outlook, physical strength and many skills, not the least a talent for improvisation. Such a mixture often fits ill into the daily peacetime barrack life but given a recovery task these men are in their element, pitting their knowledge, experience and muscle against the worst situations that fate can contrive.

# Part 1
# From Horse to Horsepower

# Chapter 1
# The Early Development of Mechanical Transport

Throughout recorded history until about two hundred years ago the limitations of man's ability in agriculture, land transport and warfare had been the power of the horse. The pace of life and of military operations was conditioned by this and could only change when a newer power source appeared. By the late eighteenth century steam power had become a practicality and the way was clear for a new industrialised world. As early as 1782 the Frenchman Cugnot had built a steam-powered gun tractor, the first attempt at applying steam to warfare. The first British proposals for the use of military steam tractors came during the Crimean War, 1854–56, but none was sent out before the war ended. Experiments began soon after, in 1857, at Woolwich under the control of the Royal Engineers (RE) and by 1873, the time of the Ashanti Wars in Africa, a number of machines was in service. Trials were carried out hauling guns and wagon trains. The term 'mechanical transport' (MT), dates from this period. Some of these early machines, like their civilian agricultural counterparts, were fitted with powered winches and were used to recover other tractors, guns or wagons which overturned or became bogged in soft ground. Whilst not designed specifically for this purpose these were in effect the first recovery vehicles.

By 1899, the beginning of the Boer War, the steam tractor had become efficient but the internal combustion (petrol) engine had been developed in the last two decades of the century and the motor car was already seen as a more practical means of light transport. A number of steam tractors and two motor cars were sent to South Africa during the war.

Up to this time MT had remained a RE responsibility but the growing civilian use of steam and petrol engined vehicles induced the War Office in 1900 to set up a Mechanical Transport Committee. The first trials of vehicles were held in 1901, all but one of the contestants being steam powered. By 1902 the Committee had recommended that MT should become the province of the Army Service Corps (ASC). Trials continued under the control of the Director of Supplies and Transport at the War Office.

Initially steam tractors and steam lorries predominated since their reliability was the product of half a century of development. Motor cars and motor lorries were at first too unreliable and fragile for military use, particularly away from firm ground or roads, but a number of far-sighted civilian enthusiasts pointed the way by volunteering private

cars and motorcycles for military manoeuvres and, on occasions, fleets of buses, cars and lorries were hired to demonstrate the strategic movement of bodies of troops by road. The power of the steam tractor at low speeds was ideal for hauling loaded wagons and heavy guns and this enabled it to hold off the competition of the motor vehicle in these roles particularly, for some years. For load carrying, however, the motor lorry soon began to emerge from the early demonstrations and trials as the leader in its field. By 1914 wheeled and tracked tractors with petrol or paraffin engines had been developed which could improve on most features of the steam tractor.

The War Office was not as slow to move with the times as is sometimes claimed. The pragmatic men of the technical Corps, RE, Army Ordnance Department (AOD) and ASC simply wanted reliable and efficient machines before making large-scale equipment purchases. The first staff cars were in service by 1903, the year in which the first ASC MT company was formed. By 1909 the annual financial estimates showed reductions in the number of horse-drawn ASC companies in favour of an increase in MT.

If not its infancy this period was certainly the adolescence of the motor vehicle. With commendable forethought the War Office issued specifications for War Department (WD) lorries and established a considerable measure of design standardisation with which manufacturers seeking contracts had to comply. The result was not only a series of very practical, robust and well-designed military vehicles but also a specification which was in advance of that then offered to civilian buyers by some manufacturers.

To increase the amount of MT which would be made available in war a subsidy scheme was devised, by which an annual retainer was paid to civilian owners of WD specification vehicles on condition that they were surrendered to the War Office if war broke out. The first scheme in 1908 was for steam vehicles. The next subsidy scheme called for petrol lorries in 30-cwt (1½-ton) and 3-ton load capacities. Most manufacturers of lorries, and there were then many more than today, produced one or more WD types. The most famous was a Leyland which was chosen by the Royal Flying Corps (RFC) to be its standard 3-tonner. The separation of the RFC in 1918 from the Army to become the Royal Air Force (RAF), led to the Leyland being known ever after as the 'RAF type'.

# Chapter 2
# The First World War: Motor Transport and Tanks

When the British Expeditionary Force (BEF) embarked for France in 1914 on the outbreak of World War I the main method of strategic military movement on land was railway transport. Extensive networks existed in Britain and France but it soon became clear that to supply the Army forward of railheads demanded far more MT than was available. MT was sought in preference to horse-drawn wagons because each 3-tonner carried three times as much as a horse-drawn General Service (GS) wagon, took up less space in a column, was less susceptible to the effects of weather and more likely to survive shelling. A few shrapnel holes in non-essential parts of a vehicle mattered not but a slightly wounded horse had to be evacuated or destroyed.

At that time, however, there were many disadvantages to the use of MT. Its reliability was relative to the technology of the age and depended entirely on skilled handling and maintenance. Whereas much of the population of Britain and France was familiar with the horse, wagon and harness, few were capable of driving let alone maintaining mechanical vehicles. To the depredations caused by poorly trained drivers were added those of the terrain. After the initial advances and retreats the war had settled down to a slogging match between two lines of fixed defences stretching from the Belgian coast through France to the Swiss border. One of the main features was intense artillery fire which reduced already poor roads to rough, shell pitted trails, totally unsuitable for any wheeled vehicle, self-powered or not; in fact pack horses, mules and human porters were sometimes the only means of supplying forward troops.

In the Middle East where Turkey was the enemy, MT suffered mainly from the effects of sand and dust and also from the absence of nearby base repair resources. In East Africa the problem was a lack of good roads and the effects of the tropical climate. Despite these problems MT was successfully employed.

The Army had available, in 1914, about 1,200 WD-type lorries of which only 80 were actually War Office owned, the remainder being subsidy vehicles. There was also a large number of ambulances and cars. A typical week's production of lorries by the whole of the British motor industry at this time was about 150. To meet immediate needs, emergency legislation was passed authorising the commandeering of civilian lorries, cars and traction engines as well as horses and wagons for war service. The result as far as MT was concerned was a still inadequate fleet of vehicles,

*ASC Siddeley Deasy Breakdown car. World War I.*

mostly non-standard, often badly worn and not robust enough for the purpose. One more useful decision was the requisitioning of over a thousand London buses. Most of them went to France complete with their colourful bus bodies but many were later converted to cargo vehicles. One unmodified survivor still exists in the London Transport Museum collection.

The longer term solution was the purchase of thousands of American, Italian and Swiss lorries. In all cases these were sturdy, well-engineered machines and some of the American types, particularly, were capable of carrying

*3-ton salvage lorry, possibly AEC Y type.*

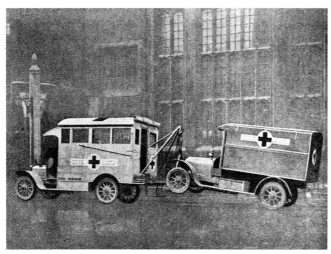

*Commer workshop and breakdown lorry of an ambulance unit.*

*Supply tank being used with another, out of sight, to right an overturned gun tank.*

greater loads than the WD types. Purchases were made later through the Ministry of Munitions which gradually took over responsibility for the provision of all war material.

The original plan for MT maintenance in France to be shared between the AOC and ASC foundered due to the hoarding of scarce spare parts by front line ASC units and eventually most MT repair was carried out by the ASC which took over the former AOC Base Repair Workshop at Rouen.

The tank came into existence for two separate reasons and was developed initially by two Services, the Navy and the Army. From the beginning of the war the Navy had operated on the left flank of the allied armies in Belgium in a ground role, naval divisions having been formed from both marines and naval reservists without ships. The Royal Naval Air Service (RNAS) supported them with reconnaissance and bombing flights and a mobile pilot rescue service was set up to save 'downed' pilots before the Germans could get to them. This service, using armed passenger cars, soon discovered the limitations of unprotected vehicles and quickly adopted armoured cars, some of quite elaborate design with machine gun armed rotating turrets. The 1914 vintage motor car with rear wheel drive only, fragile wooden or wire-spoked wheels and weak transmission soon created a quest for better cross-country vehicles. So began a train of development encouraged by an ex-soldier, the First Lord of the Admiralty, as he then was, Mr Winston Churchill.

Once the early mobile phase of the war had ended and the opposing armies had dug in, advances could only be made in the face of intense machine gun and artillery fire. The resulting enormous cost in lives brought demands from the front for a cross-country armoured vehicle capable of traversing trenches, crushing barbed wire and conveying machine-gun teams into action. Soon, and logically, the War Office plans were coordinated with the developments already started by the Navy and, eventually, a machine evolved which was rushed into production.

The design which was to dominate early armoured warfare was the now familiar rhomboid shape which

remains still on the design of the Royal Tank Regiment (RTR) cap badge. A sponson protruded on each side of the vehicle in which was mounted either two machine-guns or a 6-pounder gun. The machine was designed to cross enemy trenches. Their width dictated its length of more than 26 feet and thus a weight of nearly 30 tons. The main civilian firm involved in the design was Messrs Fosters of Lincoln but many others took part in production. The principles of tracked vehicles were, by 1915, well understood. In the USA tracked agricultural tractors were already in use and similar machines had been built in England though not adopted commercially.

The name given by the Navy to the new device during its early involvement was 'landship' and for a time this stuck: but the secrecy surrounding the project was enhanced by marking early vehicles as 'tanks', their rivetted panel construction resembling to some degree large water tanks. This crisp security code-name soon attached itself to the new vehicle and no official redesignation since that time has succeeded in changing it.

When the first tanks went into action in 1916 contemporary military vehicles were steam and paraffin powered tractors weighing 10 to 15 tons and the American Holt tractors weighing about 12 tons. The heaviest motor lorries were some of the imported types with a laden weight of about 8 tons. Tanks, at nearly 30 tons, were therefore in all respects monsters and while they struck terror into those Germans they confronted they also caused great logistic problems for the British Army.

The tank was to be operated by a new corps but again for reasons of secrecy it was first known as the Heavy Section of the Machine Gun Corps (MGC). By the time some vehicles had been captured by the Germans the name 'tank' was well known and no need remained for euphemism, so the new organisation was free to proclaim itself as the Tank Corps. The word 'Royal' was added to the Corps' title shortly after the war ended and also to the AOC and ASC in recognition of their outstanding war service.

In common with other heavy machines, the tank had to be designed for carriage by rail. This dictated that the side sponsons must be detachable, since the width of the main body of the tank was already close to the UK railway loading gauge of approximately 9 feet. Any movement away from railways had to be on the tank's own tracks, either self-powered or towed. In France and Belgium the semi-static nature of the war enabled railway lines to be constructed well forward. From the railhead, the approach march over poor roads with underpowered and completely unsprung vehicles meant that in the tank's first battle so many broke down that only six crossed the start line.

The War Office was very keen to get tanks into action, confidently expecting them to reduce the appalling infantry casualties. Few, if any, obstacles were placed in the way of the new weapon's development and much thought went into the organisation to operate and support it. 711 MT Company ASC initially provided drivers and vehicle maintenance support whilst AOD officers and AOC trades-men (then in separate Corps) were involved from the start in maintaining the tank's armament. The Heavy Section (later Heavy Branch) MGC provided tank crews, headquarters staff, engineering officers and many repair tradesmen. As tanks were shipped to France for stockpiling, others were sent to Bovington in Dorset, where the new Corps' depot and training unit was established. The operational base in France included a static workshop (later titled Tank Corps Central Workshop). In the haste to get tanks into action the headquarters in France failed to realise the difficulties inherent in the introduction of an entirely new weapon concept; machines of uncertain reliability whose crews and supporting organisation lacked experience. It was inevit-able, perhaps, that the tank achieved very limited success in the Somme battle but its potential was clearly seen and development continued. Soon tanks were organised in battalions, each with its own mobile workshop, but this concept quickly changed when workshops were combined into larger units leaving a handful of tradesmen in each battalion to supervise tank crews in maintenance and simple repairs.

As the size of the Tank Corps in France increased and casualties throughout the Army created severe manpower shortages the need arose for greater productivity from the small numbers of skilled tradesmen available to the technical corps. The engineer officers in both the Tank Corps and the AOD, using their knowledge of production organisation, redeployed the tradesmen for maximum output, leading inevitably to the thinning out of front-line tradesmen, almost to their disappearance. This created more static workshops where engineering considerations could be given more emphasis but was only feasible in the static warfare conditions of the Western Front.

Soon after tanks went into action in 1916 a crisis arose over the supply of the 6-pounder guns, as the Navy needed to retain stocks to equip light craft and for the defence against German submarines which often attacked merchant vessels using gunnery to save torpedoes. Whereas many of the derelict tanks littering the battlefields were deemed unsalvageable it was now important to at least recover the guns. A salvage party under Captain R.P. Butler, a former RE officer, set about retrieving guns and soon found some of the tanks themselves to be repairable or at least to have other salvageable components. From this beginning there grew up first one then two tank-salvage companies. Among the soldiers serving in the first company for a time were a number of Australians detached from the 29th Australian Infantry Battalion. Later, the companies were amalgamated to form an advanced field workshop, known as the Tank Field Battalion, to carry out field repairs. This left the Central Workshop to concentrate on overhauls, major rebuilds and the repair and reclamation of components and assemblies. The men of the salvage companies were the first to be involved in tank recovery in the field.

# Chapter 3
# First World War Salvage Systems and Equipment

Recovery of MT, like maintenance, was mainly an ASC responsibility. One of the pioneers in the development of recovery vehicles was the 1st Mobile Repair Unit of 93 Company ASC. A detailed account of the design of its recovery equipment and its employment exists in a long letter sent home by Corporal Sydney Burrows to his local vicar for inclusion in the church magazine's special Christmas issue for 1916. The repair unit specialised in recovery

*Salvage lorry showing jib, winch man and the modified canopy rails.*

*Leyland salvage lorry.*

and developed recovery vehicles by fitting cargo lorries with locally fabricated cranes or sheerlegs and hand-operated winches. The winch was positioned in the front of the lorry body with space for four men to operate it. As the requirement for recovery vehicles increased a second recovery unit was formed and more lorries were converted for its use. Gradually more sophisticated equipment was developed and built by the repair units. Devices included pulley blocks to provide mechanical advantage when winching, ground anchors of a spiral design, used originally for securing parked aircraft when strong winds threatened, and a dummy axle or ambulance which enabled severely damaged vehicles to be towed to workshops. These converted vehicles were usually known as 'salvage lorries' and sometimes as 'first aid lorries'. This use of medical terminology was to be perpetuated in the reference to 'vehicle casualties' and in other ways in later years.

A favourite chassis for the improved salvage lorries was the American Peerless which was fitted with a well-designed crane boom and supporting struts which could be placed on the ground to take the weight of the rear of the vehicle while lifting. The canopy rails were designed with a longitudinal slot to accept the crane boom. The wheels for the dummy axle were stowed on the side members of the lorry chassis behind the rear wheels giving it the appearance of a 6-wheeler.

The opportunity was taken to use any gun tractors or passing tanks for recovery. Gun tractors, wheeled and tracked, were mostly fitted with winches. A particularly useful vehicle, never available in sufficient numbers solely

*Peerless salvage lorry showing rear jack lowered and dummy axle wheels stowed on the side of the chassis.*

*Salvage lorry with dummy axle set up and rear jack raised under tailboard.*

for use on recovery, was the American Holt tractor. This in its original form was a half-track, the front supported and steered by a steel roller. The rear tracks gave it a useful off-road performance and incorporated a steering system by track brakes. The patent for this system had been purchased before the war from the British firm Ruston and Hornsby. Holts were widely employed as heavy gun tractors. A popular American lorry was the FWD made by the Four Wheel Drive Auto Company. Despite solid tyres the added traction of 4-wheel drive made the FWD a

*FWD salvage lorry with substantial girder crane.*

*A Holt tractor tows another disabled Holt.*

practical gun tractor for medium artillery. It was also a pointer to the cross-country military lorry of the future. Some FWDs were converted to recovery vehicles, one being used by the Central MT Depot in London. Despite the variety of mechanical recovery equipment there was never enough available and many a motor lorry suffered the indignity of being recovered by horses.

Tank recovery presented tremendous problems. A sound tank could tow another on firm level ground, which was practical in the workshop area but rarely so on the battlefield, where most tanks became casualties. Here was an unending panorama of trenches and shell holes, often a sea of mud. In these circumstances towing was almost impossible: sound tanks had to be dug out and damaged ones repaired *in situ* or cannibalised and abandoned. Self-recovery of 'bogged' tanks was first tried by fitting long extension 'spuds' on to track plates so that bellied tanks could get some grip on solid ground. A better solution proved to be an unditching beam, a baulk of timber chained across both tracks and drawn under them as they spun, eventually providing a solid purchase. The most common expedient was many men with shovels, still today the basic recovery tools. Repair on the spot was always the preliminary to recovery to proper workshop facilities. Gas cutting or welding equipment was rarely available then, and rivets of damaged plates often had to be heated and punched out or drilled out with hand drills. Early experiments with German hand-grenades led to their use for cutting plates and straightening running gear! Jacks, gun planks and sheerlegs for lifting were commonplace aids in recovery operations. The chief limitations were enemy shelling, terrain and weather.

*Salvage lorry with disabled staff car.*

There were many proposals for variants of the tank although few were built. One which got into production was a gun carrier, designed to carry heavy artillery pieces over broken ground. Lack of engine power and other design limitations condemned this equipment mainly to a resupply role, but before they were built two of the planned fifty were earmarked for conversion to salvage tanks and were fitted with power operated slewing cranes. They proved very useful in the Central and Depot Workshops but were too conspicuous to be practical in forward areas. Instead early marks of tank were adapted by the fitting of a set of sheerlegs to the front to act as mobile cranes. Lifting was by block and tackle. When these tanks were permanently available in this role they would also be used as tank tugs, thus representing the nearest equivalent to an Armoured Recovery Vehicle (ARV) that this war produced. There was no attempt to create a purpose built or winch-equipped recovery vehicle suitable for front-line use, the most likely reason being the relatively low power of available engines and the need to concentrate on producing gun tanks. That the Tank Corps tradesmen, even allowing for their extraordinary skills, were able to bring back any damaged and derelict tanks at all was an outstanding achievement.

By 1917 the lighter 'medium' tanks were in production, but their numbers were relatively few and their weight of 14 tons did little to ease front-line recovery difficulties. The medium tank's role was pursuit after a breakthrough by the heavy tanks of the earlier designs. It was only through an enormously expanded tank production rate that the Corps had been able to cope with irretrievable tank losses and still build up the huge reserves needed for the major tank battles of Cambrai and Amiens. In 1918 Germany launched a massive surprise offensive with initial success but the country and army was too exhausted to sustain such activity and the allies drove the Germans back. The Armistice followed in November 1918.

Little is recorded of the salvage work on the relatively few tanks used against Turkey in the Middle East but,

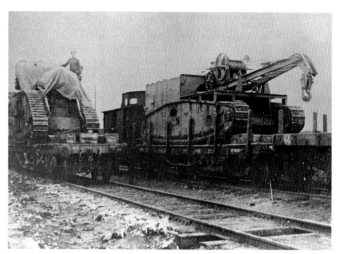

*One of two crane equipped salvage tanks based on the gun carrier hull.*

generally, terrain there was much less broken up by concentrated shelling, and it was therefore much easier to tow broken down tanks using fit tanks or heavy tractors. Armoured cars were operated by the Army in all the theatres of operations but their recovery was more akin to that employed for MT except that, being somewhat heavier, only the larger salvage lorries could be used to lift or tow them.

*Gun tank modified to salvage tank shown at a TA camp a few years after World War I ended.*

# Part 2
# **Scrimp and Save: 1919 to 1939**

# Chapter 1
# Changes in the War Office and the Army's Repair Organisations

Armistice day in November 1918 brought to an end the war against Germany and her allies. The British Army, by then mainly conscripts or volunteers for war service only, was rapidly scaled down despite increased responsibilities in the post-war period due to many additional policing tasks. To the pre-war duties of controlling the Empire were now added the occupation of Germany and for a time part of Turkey, the added commitment of Palestine, internal security in Ireland and assistance to the anti-bolshevik White Russians. Conscription continued till 1920 and much effort went into the recruiting of new regular soldiers.

Of the new mechanised branches of the Army the RASC had no difficulty retaining its MT which had proved more economical than horsed transport, a factor carrying much weight in peace time: tanks, however, were seen by few in power to have a peace-time role and the now Royal Tank Corps (RTC) was reduced to the UK Depot and four battalions with small detachments overseas mostly using armoured cars.

The cavalry had been little used in the static warfare of the Western Front but nevertheless continued after the war to have a disproportionate influence on Army affairs. This enabled it to resist the start of mechanisation until 1928. In 1939 the cavalry regiments, by then almost all in an armoured role, were combined with the RTC to form the Royal Armoured Corps (RAC).

After World War I the Ministry of Munitions ceased to exist and the War Office regained full responsibility for designing, testing and procuring vehicles and equipment. MT remained the responsibility of the RASC and an experimental department was set up in P Company RASC. Its functions included vehicle development and trials in conjunction with civilian manufacturers.

In 1919 the War Office formed a Mechanical Transport Advisory Board to coordinate the foreseen increased use of MT throughout the Army. By 1927, the mechanisation of the Army generally had progressed to the stage where it was more logical to treat MT as routine equipment rather than something peculiar. Therefore, following a 1927 War Office reorganisation, the RAOC, in January 1928, took over responsibility for MT issues to all parts of the Army other than to the RASC. The RAOC was controlled in the War Office by the Master General of Ordnance (MGO) whereas the RASC came under the Quarter Master General (QMG), reflecting the RASC responsibility for supplying food and

fuel, as important a function as transport. At the same time the classification of all vehicles was begun: 'A' vehicles included tanks, armoured cars, lorry mounted guns and half tracks. Later, fully tracked gun tractors were added to this list. 'B' vehicles were MT vehicles operated by any branch of the Army other than the RASC. RASC vehicles were simply 'B' vehicles operated by the RASC which thus sought to retain something of its original pre-eminence in this field.

For a time after 1918 the Department of Tank Design and Experiment (DTD & E) continued to function under its head, Colonel P. Johnson, an RTC engineering officer, and was transferred, in 1921, to the Superintendent of Design's Department at the Royal Arsenal, Woolwich. Work concentrated on the Medium D, an improved wartime design now fitted with suspension. Other versions were made as amphibious tanks but no series production was undertaken. Then, in 1923, for economy reasons, the DTD & E was closed down and the War Office sought designs for new tanks from traditional armaments manufacturers starting, at this time, to add this weapon to their stock in trade. Tank designers remaining in the Superintendent of Design's department were, in 1928, transferred to the Directorate of Mechanization, part of the MGO's department. Their role was now relegated to liaison with the commercial suppliers and minor modification work. Some complete designs were produced during the later rearmament period and put into production but most tank design at this time was the work of commercial firms. The War office sought B and RASC vehicles from motor manufacturers by providing design specifications, testing prototypes and then placing orders.

All the corps involved in mechanical transport and traction took part, either jointly or separately, in the trials of new vehicles. The RAOC was concerned with their recovery and repair and the RE with their compatibility with military bridges. The seemingly complicated structure for the control of procurement, testing and operation of mechanical vehicles functioned reasonably well since the Army and War Office were small; most of the experimental work was carried out by enthusiasts whose engineering training overrode inter-corps rivalry and the scale of operation was minimal. It was not till 1936 that the total Army post-World War I MT holdings reached 4,000 world-wide and at that time there were but a few hundred tanks.

From 1933, however, a new threat to peace became

apparent from Nazi Germany and to the already complex problem of mechanisation was soon added the quantitative problems of rearmament, i.e. the providing of modern equipment for the regular and reserve armies. The War Office departments dealing with equipment design and provision were frequently reorganised in an effort to cope, but increases in staff rather than a reshuffle of responsibilities would have had more impact. A major step was the setting up of a Directorate of Munitions Production but the benefits of this were quickly lost when this, together with its subordinate MGO's department and directorates, was absorbed in 1939 into the newly created Ministry of Supply (MOS). Having surrendered almost all its technical branches to the new Ministry, the War Office lacked, for the crucial first year of World War II, any branch with the expertise to produce technical specifications or directives which the MOS could work to when designing military equipment. Trials establishments too were transferred so new military organisations had to be formed to conduct user trials of machines designed by the civilian ministry. In fact, as the war progressed hundreds of servicemen were seconded to the MOS and the cross-flow of ideas and complaints concerning equipment did not depend entirely on the rigid inter-departmental channels of communciation. Nevertheless this severing of the War Office equipment branches was a constituent cause of much of the delay and design errors which bedevilled equipment development in the early years of the war.

The frequent trials and manoeuvres of army units and formations in the 1920s and early 1930s were meant to establish tactical concepts and to show what, if any, reorganisation was required to meet the needs of, and realise the potential of, mechanisation. Conclusions were slow in coming and theorists had a field day. The War Office moved uncertainly but did, before World War II began, decide to form an armoured division. The Regular Army field force in the United Kingdom in the pre-Munich crisis period scarcely amounted to two divisions-worth of troops. They were rarely exercised in their field formations and were still far from fully mechanised, so the scale of repair and recovery support cobbled together for manoeuvres gave little indication of the full needs of wartime operations, particularly of an army that was to be increased in size at a rate far outstripping the resources available to support it.

To be fair, some enlightened officers of RAOC(E) had written papers in the 1930s forecasting accurately the effects of mobile warfare on their Corps and the changes which should be made to provide effective repair and recovery support. For the most part they were unable to influence the pre-war organisation as technical training was not thought a proper background for dictating Corps organisation. In any case funds were scarce in peace time for increasing strengths of manpower or equipment, the main solutions to RAOC(E)'s problems.

Between the wars the system for repairs was brought more up to date since it was thought likely that the next war would be more mobile. Time would then become the dominating factor so any repair work which would take too long in a unit or a mobile workshop would have to be passed back to a static workshop. The repair organisation in fighting units had to be greatly strengthened to cope with mechanisation. The RASC trained its drivers to a high level of technical competence and backed this with the transport company's own workshop platoon. The RTC had driver mechanics supported by unit tradesmen but was reinforced in each battalion (later regiment) by an RAOC LAD. As the RA and cavalry became mechanised their units were to receive LADs. At first these LADs were found by detaching men and equipment from the larger RAOC mobile workshops but eventually they were separately and permanently established for each task. RAOC(E) repair responsibilities increased with mechanisation and Army expansion but its manpower remained totally inadequate for the workload, a situation that was to continue well into the war.

The more advanced workshop organisations in the Middle East had come into use after experience during the military action in the late 1930s in Palestine and after the thorough and professional training carried out in Egypt before the action began against the Italians in Libya. While the Middle East remained the only war theatre where the Army was actively engaged against the enemy it was inevitably the forcing house of new tactical and logistic ideas and procedures.

Breakdown vehicles were provided in RASC and RAOC workshops and in LADs but no separate recovery units existed until after the outbreak of war. When a recovery task proved too difficult for a unit or its LAD the next line of support was the RAOC mobile workshop. Drivers were, however, expected to be self sufficient to a great degree and all received at least elementary recovering training. The Manual of Driving and Maintenance – Mechanical Vehicles (Wheeled), issued by the War Office in 1937 to all units with MT, covered in elaborate detail the means of self-help recovery even to the extent of using the resources of the 'local blacksmith' before, if all else failed, 'calling the breakdown gang'. They were destined to find few village blacksmiths in the deserts of North Africa!

# Chapter 2
# Equipment Design in the 1920s and 1930s

Everyone believed that World War I was 'the war to end all wars'. This was enshrined in Government policy in a 'ten-year rule' dangerously assuming that there would be no other major continental war for ten years. For reasons, one suspects, of fiscal expediency this period was continually extended. The Treasury, guardians of the nation's war-depleted wealth, armed with the ten-year rule and knowing the vast legacy of usable equipment remaining in Army depots, felt justified in pruning from Army Estimates much of the funds for developing and providing new equipment. Although huge weapon stocks remained, the bulk of the 200,000 motor vehicles in use at the end of World War I had been sold off. Those remaining quickly became obsolete.

When the war ended, contracts for the vast numbers of tanks needed for Plan 1919 were cancelled. Extant at the time was an initial production contract for Medium C tanks, a development of the Medium A used towards the end of the war, and 36 of these were completed. The Tank Corps, reduced in size and with these newer and smaller tanks, needed few of the older heavy tanks, so surplus machines were sold to friendly governments and many others became war memorials. Operational plans, evolving as the war ended, convinced the RTC that future wars would be more mobile and so, although some heavy tanks were still used for training, and from 1921 by the newly re-established Territorial Army (TA), the future was seen to lie with the faster mediums. For a few years the Medium Cs and a handful of experimental Medium Ds were the only ones which could, by any stretch of the imagination, be regarded as modern. Despite this and the insecure future of the RTC the potential of armour was recognised by such pundits as Major General J.F.C. Fuller and Captain B.H. Liddell-Hart. Both foresaw the mobile warfare that was to characterise the next major conflict and did their best to influence developments accordingly.

There had been much progress during World War I towards improving the reliability and practical value of MT and there were even better prospects, given experiment and development. Four-wheel drive, the use of shaft drive instead of chain drive, wider use of pneumatic tyres even on some 3-tonners, heavier capacity lorries and the use of caterpillar tracks all brought nearer the realisation of the concept of a fully mechanised army whose vehicles would no longer depend on roads. More forward thinking and dedicated officers therefore fought for and gained a meagre

budget which enabled the post-war Army to keep abreast of new developments in transport and tanks and to carry out small scale experiments and purchases.

Under RAOC control B vehicle storage and issues were gradually concentrated at Farnborough near Aldershot. A vehicles remained for a time at Woolwich. The RASC MT depot was set up at Feltham, Middlesex. Farnborough was also the site of the Mechanical Warfare Experimental Establishment (MWEE) which from 1928 took over the role of P Company and also carried out A Vehicle trials, though some experiments continued at Woolwich and at Boving-ton. In 1934 MWEE became the Mechanisation Experimental Establishment (MEE).

Tracked vehicle trials centred on reliability of engines and tracks. Most development work was now done by the manufacturers. In 1922 Vickers had produced the prototype of what was to become the Vickers Medium tank. This went into production a year later and about 160 (of two Marks) were built. They became the standard tank of the RTC up to the beginning of rearmament in the late 1930s. Weighing, in the developed versions, approximately 12 tons and with a speed of 16-mph, these tanks were light years ahead of all that had been developed until then. A front-mounted air-cooled Armstrong Siddeley V8 engine provided power and the armament was a 47mm (3-pounder) gun with up to six machine guns mounted or carried. These were the tanks used in all the experimental manoeuvres of the late 1920s and early 1930s, which were to puzzle the tacticians and doctrine writers in the War Office whilst enlightening Britain's future enemies.

Following on the heels of the Vickers Medium tank came a spawning of one-man and two-man 'tankettes' and machine gun carriers, many from the designs of Sir John Carden, whose company was eventually absorbed by Vickers. One of the two important production designs was the series of 5-ton light tanks armed only with machine guns, ideal together with armoured cars for the colonial policing role. The second design, a machine gun carrier for the Infantry, led to the Universal Carrier, used for many purposes and in huge numbers in World War II and generally known as the 'Bren Carrier'.

Armoured cars developed during the 1930s began by making use of the 6×4 drive system and like those of World War I retained machine gun armament. By 1939 the first modern designs with 4-wheel drive and heavier armament had appeared, some having all drive line components attached directly to the hull armour instead of having a separate chassis. Here too cost considerations intervened and so as well as the first few modern armoured cars, new vehicles in use at the beginning of World War II included cheaply armoured versions of Morris Commercial 15-cwt trucks. The 1920 pattern Rolls Royce, an updated World War I design, still equipped some units twenty years after its introduction.

By the mid 1930s the Vickers Medium tanks were obsolescent and in any case too few in number when some thoughts in the War Office began to crystallise on the concept of armoured divisions. Vickers' first improved design, the Medium Mark III or '16-tonner' was condemned partly on grounds of cost and only three were built. Later other manufacturers were invited to start taking an interest in tank design. Their problems were not only inexperience but, like Vickers, they were continually foiled by the absence of, or changes to, War Office policy on tank employment as the pros and contras, by virtue of the system of two and three year appointments in the War Office, came and went.

One of the reasons for the under-funding of new tank design and purchasing was the emphasis placed on the needs of Air Defence of Great Britain (ADGB) including, as it did, fighter aircraft, Anti Aircraft (AA) guns and radar. The expansion and modernisation of the Navy as prime protector of the 'island fortress' together with increases in Coast Artillery were also given priority, as was the funding of Civil Defence. These could be seen as defensive measures whereas tanks were deemed offensive at a time when the League of Nations was striving for disarmament.

Despite these problems some advances in tank design were made. Two important steps were the adoption of the tank suspension system designed by the American J. Walter Christie and of a tank transmission and steering unit developed by Dr H. Merrit from a basic concept by Mr W.G. Wilson, one of the main designers of World War I tanks. Another positive decision taken at this time decreed that there would be two classes of tank, a light, fast 'Cruiser' for mobile operations and a slower, more heavily armoured 'Infantry' tank to storm fortified positions in support of infantry on foot. These distinctions persisted till the end of World War II. Yet another decision standardised the main armament for all types of gun-armed tank with the new infantry anti-tank gun, the 2-pounder. Cost considerations caused the first infantry tank to be so small that it could only accommodate machine gun armanent. Its successor, the Matilda was probably the best tank in the world when it first appeared, an accolade it would soon lose when the impetus of war hastened tank development in all the countries involved. The cruiser tanks built in the immediate pre-war period were for the most part barely adequate for their task due to rushed development, unfamiliarity by manufacturers and underfunding. Not surprisingly, those built by the experienced firm Vickers were usually rated mechanically reliable.

In the case of B and RASC vehicle development much more impetus came from the Army itself. In the 1920s experiments were conducted with three main classes of vehicle, the 4-wheel drive lorry and tractor, the half-track and later the rigid 6-wheeler. This designation distinguished it from the tractor/semi-trailer combination or articulated 6-wheeler. Early experiments with 4-wheel drive centred on the Hathi, the prototype of which was built by P Company RASC based on parts of a German Erhardt tractor. Later 25 production Hathis were built for the Army by Thornycrofts, starting in 1924. Most were used as gun

14  Thornycroft Hathi breakdown lorry c 1926.

14A  Rear view of the Thornycroft Hathi breakdown lorry.

tractors whilst one at least was fitted with a breakdown body and lasted into the late 1930s. It had a jib at the rear with a hand operated jib winch. Another recovery version was used by the RAF. Whilst it was undoubtedly a powerful tractor, the technology for the driven and steered axle was at that time both unreliable and expensive, so the Hathi gave way to the 6-wheeler with the rear four wheels driven, the 6×4.

Half-tracks, using French 'Kegresse' tracks or the British 'Roadless' system, each replacing the rear wheels of a conventional car or lorry, were for a time seen as the best means of off-road movement. However, their cost, weight and heavy wear on roads were a disadvantage. Comparative trials conducted in the 1920s at Aldershot and at Bovington showed that, overall, 6-wheeled lorries with four driven wheels were adequate for most off-road conditions and would be cheaper to produce and maintain than half tracks. Despite this, a small number of half-track gun tractors was purchased and some, Burfords and Morris Commercials, were sent to Shanghai in 1927 when the International Settlement was reinforced during the Chinese Civil War.

The first 6-wheelers evolved in 1918 in the USA through experiments by the Goodyear Tyre Company. The use of a double-drive rear bogie built by the Templin Company combined with new Goodyear pneumatic tyres produced a vehicle which was more economical, faster and for a given engine size able to carry more. Soon 6-wheelers were developed in France and Britain with and without both rear axles driven, but for military purposes double-drive was essential to increase traction in soft ground.

The commercial 6-wheelers were improved by a War Office designed and patented rear bogie. The 1925 patent described a system using two springs, one above and one below a central pivot attached to each of the two chassis side members. The two rear axles were shackled between each set of springs so that they retained their position relative to one another. The system was aided by radius rods and overcame the tendency in other designs for a wheel to lift when moving cross-country, causing a loss of drive to the wheel still grounded through normal differential action. Early versions, including recovery vehicles, had twin rear wheels and high pressure tyres.

The MT Advisory Board used its powers to organise experiments jointly with civilian industry and among its more important achievements were the low pressure cross-country tyre and, later, the sand tyre. With the War Department (WD) rear bogie and the new low-pressure cross-country tyres the 6-wheeler was the equal of contemporary half-tracks except in very soft mud or snow. The bogie design enabled overall tracks or chains to be fitted effectively converting it to a half-track if need be. To meet the requirements for this type of vehicle a specification was issued and the War Office freely surrendered its patent rights for the WD bogie to manufacturers contracted to supply vehicles for the Army. The WD type 6-wheeler was perfected by the mid-1930s and it was again hoped that the numbers required in war might be provided in peace time through a subsidy scheme as in World War I. One scheme had already been tried for 4-wheelers in the 30-cwt class but with only limited success. A new subsidy scheme based on the WD 6-wheeler was even less successful. The inducements were insufficient for civilian users who, by the 1930s, could buy nominal 3-ton payload 4×2 lorries capable of taking nearly 100 per cent overloads, and which were both cheaper and more economical to run than the heavy WD types. The military and civilian requirements were no longer compatible. This torpedoed the plan for standardisation on 6×4 vehicles and, accepting reluctantly that funds would not permit the outright purchase of all the Army's needs, the War Office devised a new plan: the 6×4 lorries would be the standard front-line vehicles supported in rear areas by less sophisticated civilian-pattern vehicles.

The increasing need for mechanisation brought requirements for other classes of vehicles, light and heavy utilities, 8-cwt and 15-cwt trucks and both 6- and 10-ton lorries. Trials were conducted of many civilian vehicles designed to meet these new specifications. The failure of the 6×4 lorry subsidy scheme caused the War Office to examine the contemporary mass-produced vehicles available in the 3-ton class. Trials in the 1930s led to a new category of WD 3-ton 4×2 truck which, when fitted with single, low-pressure cross-country tyres, was deemed suitable for lines of communication (L of C) transport. These vehicles had the advantage of cheapness and ready availability from existing production lines and were just coming into Army service as World War II began. This financial expedient was later to be regretted and most manufacturers were asked to develop 4×4 3-tonners a year or so later. Even so there were never enough of these to fully equip the field armies with proper cross-country vehicles.

# Chapter 3
# Recovery Vehicles in the Inter-War Period

The better of the World War I recovery vehicle designs were adequate, for a time, to deal with the quite small numbers of MT vehicles remaining in service in the early 1920s. American chassis soon gave way to British and as the first 6-wheelers were developed some were built with winches and recovery equipment. The dummy axle or 'ambulance' used in World War I was further developed and some were built incorporating jibs. During this period the first gantry breakdown bodies appeared. These consisted of a strong girder structure integral with a cargo body and looking like a set of reinforced canopy rails. Below the upper cross-members of this structure a longitudinal 'I' beam was fitted which could be slid forward for travelling, protruding over the driving cab, or rearwards to support another vehicles on suspended tow. Lifting was by block and tackle or a hand-operated winch attached to the end of the I beam. The front of the beam could be unshipped and clamped to the floor of the vehicle which raised the rear end above roof level, enabling the device to be used as a crane. Originally these bodies were built on both 30-cwt and 3-ton chassis. The design lasted well into the 1950s in Army service, albeit on more modern chassis. The Royal Navy was still using a gantry-bodied recovery vehicle in 1986. The 3-ton chassis for these vehicles were, in most cases, fitted with 5-ton winches and were rated in the 1930s as heavy breakdown vehicles. Production 3-tonners were on Leyland Retriever, Crossley IGL7 and IGL8 and Guy

*A Crossley IGL7 3-ton breakdown gantry lorry showing the jib raised and ramps for loading a dummy axle.*

FBAX chassis. Most gantry lorries were used then by the RAOC since the high lift capability was essential for A vehicle engine changes. The need for a high mounting point for the I beam made the gantry body much higher than the normal cargo body on the same chassis and thus very difficult to conceal when in action.

An alternative and less well-known contemporary breakdown lorry was a much simpler type. Based on the standard cargo body common to the 6×4 range of 3-ton lorries the basic breakdown lorry had a girder crane of fixed height bolted to the vehicle chassis through the floor. It was fitted with bracing struts at the rear of the vehicle and could support about 2½ tons, enough to lift one end of another 3-tonner on suspended tow. A hand-operated jib-winch was fitted. This style of recovery equipment was sometimes known as a Weaver crane. The Weaver Manufacturing and Engineering Co Ltd was a well-known builder of garage equipment. These breakdown lorries were produced mainly

*Morris Commercial D type 30 cwt gantry lorry with machine gun carrier on two wheeled trailer.*

on the Thornycroft WO/AC/4, the Albion WD 131 and BY3 and the Karrier FM6A and CK6 chassis. Most were used by the RASC and, like most pre-war vehicles, a great number was lost when the Army was evacuated from France in 1940. It was, however, cheaper and easier to replace than the more complex gantry lorry.

In addition to gantry bodies built on the 30-cwt 6×4 chassis, some of the RAOC workshop tool lorries on the Morris Commercial D Type chassis were fitted with lifting booms at the rear, but these were not such effective recovery vehicles having no main winch. By the late 1930s only Morris Commercial were still building military 30-cwt

*RASC 3-ton 6×4 breakdown lorry showing details of jib structure.*

6×4 chassis. The CD and then CDSW superseded the original D Type. One version of the CDSW was a light breakdown lorry. It had a 4-ton chassis winch and the rear of the body consisted of equipment lockers. A small A frame jib was fitted at the rear of the chassis. Production of these continued well into World War II.

*Morris Commercial CDSW light breakdown tractor.*

*FWD R6T Heavy Breakdown Tractor with Taskers light tank transporter trailer carrying Vickers Light Tank Mark II.*

*FWD R6T with tubular steel jib in use for Ordnance officer training at Bovington.*

The Four Wheel Drive Auto Co had set up an agency in Slough to refurbish ex-World War I FWDs for sale on the civilian market and this then progressed to the manufacture of new designs. Eventually the firm separated from the parent company and, in 1927, began to produce a 6-wheel drive tractor developed from an earlier lorry. The Army adopted this model, the R6T, in 1929, as a gun tractor and a heavy breakdown tractor variant for the RAOC soon followed. Both types had 7-ton winches. In all 61 R6Ts were built between 1929 and 1936. The breakdown vehicles provided the RAOC(E) with the means of recovering most of the A and B vehicles in use at the time. Two variants of the FWD recovery vehicles are recorded, one with a crane consisting of an angled girder A frame surmounted by a horizontal jib and the other a simpler tubular A frame with a pulley at the apex. Early R6Ts were powered by Dorman engines. By the end of R6T production the British FWD company had been absorbed by AEC, the latter having supplied the 110 bhp engine used in later vehicles for some time. After the take over the tractors were known as AEC R6Ts. Although it had 6-wheel drive the artillery tractor was barely robust enough to cope with the more heavy World War I guns then being modernised. Similarly, new tanks on the drawing board then would be too heavy for the breakdown tractor. There was clearly a need for a heavier tractor for both roles by 1936 when the last R6T was built.

Messrs G. Scammell and Nephew began vehicle production soon after World War I and quickly established an enviable reputation in the motor industry for soundly engineered and robust vehicles. The firm specialised in heavy load carriers and tractors, producing 6×4 and 6×6 vehicles in the 1920s, mainly for oilfield work. From this design, named the Pioneer, three military vehicles were developed. The main feature of this chassis was its suspension and transmission system. A single rear axle drove two wheels on each side by means of an enclosed gear train, the casings for which pivoted on the ends of the axle allowing much greater wheel movement than would be possible with a conventional double drive bogie. The front axle was attached to a transverse leaf spring pivoted at the centre and was positioned by a horizontal A frame with its apex under the vehicle's gearbox. This ingenious, if complicated, arrangement gave the vehicle a cross-country performance unparalleled for its time.

The Army carried out trials with a second-hand Pioneer in about 1927 and purchased a purpose-designed armoured car chassis in 1928. After trials it seems that its wooden mock-up body was discarded and the vehicle converted to a breakdown lorry. It remained for many years in this role at MWEE Farnborough. In 1932 the first Scammell Pioneer

articulated transporter was purchased. Details of this vehicle are given on page 20. A gun tractor was later designed and then a heavy breakdown tractor. These two had a common chassis and production versions were fitted with a vertical 8-ton chassis winch. Earlier Pioneers had used a horizontal winch. With the recovery tackle carried on the breakdown tractor its winch capacity was adequate for most recovery work, but was by no means generous when dealing with tanks and some of the heavier transport vehicles which were to come into use during the Pioneer's long period of service.

The first production Scammell breakdown tractor was delivered in 1939 and was given the model designation SVIS. Its recovery crane consisted of a narrow A frame of girder construction with a horizontal I beam jib at the top. The jib was held in the horizontal position by two struts and the whole structure folded forward into the body well for travelling. This over-complex structure was replaced, after about fifty had been built, by the more common Herbert Morris sliding jib, the bottom section of which remained fixed in the body at an angle of about 35° from horizontal. An extending section could be slid out to increase reach and height for use when towing or lifting. A hand operated winch was used for lifting. This version of the breakdown tractor was the SV2S. In both versions equipment was

*Scammell Model SV1S with jib erected.*

carried in two timber lockers, one each side of the recovery jib. A rack under the right hand side of the cab carried steel tracks which could be fitted over the pair of rear wheels on each side to convert the vehicle effectively into a half-track for traversing very soft ground. Counterweights, on brackets in front of the radiator, served to balance the load when towing a vehicle suspended from the jib.

The Scammells were, for their time, massive vehicles, nearly one foot wider than the then permitted maximum for commercial vehicles, and weighing approximately 10 tons unladen. The breakdown tractor and gun tractor used 13.50 × 20 tyres. Unusually for this period production Pioneers were diesel engined. The Gardner 6LW was already a well established engine in commercial use and despite its relatively low output a transmission with six forward gears enabled Scammells to move prodigious loads. Above the radiator header tank the vehicle carried a distinctive round extension chamber giving rise to the name 'coffee pot' Scammell. Another name arising from the use of a diesel engine was 'the knocker'.

By 1940 the Matilda tank was coming into service weighing about 25 tons, twice the weight of Vickers Mediums of the early 1930s. The wheeled breakdown vehicle was at this time, together with the first few tank transporters, the only means of recovering tanks needing more than just a tow, so the size and power of the new Scammells were in every way justified. Some of the 1,700 Pioneer breakdown tractors built were issued to the RAF and some to other Empire armies.

A contemporary development was the AEC Matador which, although adopted primarily as a gun tractor, was to be extensively used in the recovery role in the Middle East. The Matador was originally a civilian 4-wheeled lorry in the AEC commercial range. An off-shoot of the British FWD Company, Hardy Motors, which had specialised in building 4-wheel-drive conversions, was absorbed by AEC together with the FWD company and the 4×4 Matador was built using Hardy developed components. Despite not being accepted during military cargo vehicle trials, it was selected instead for use as a tractor for the 6-inch howitzer and 3.7-inch AA gun. Like the Scammell, most AEC Matadors were diesel engined and were fitted with 7-ton chassis

winches. The Matador used 13.50 × 20 cross-country tyres, giving it an excellent off-road performance. This, together with the winch, made it a most suitable vehicle for recovery work. Somewhat strangely, no official recovery version seems to have been built for Army use.

An ideal means of recovery from the cost viewpoint was the dummy axle or ambulance. These had appeared during World War I and were developed in the inter-war period. One was a simple T bar with a small solid tyred twin wheeled bogie on each side which could be fitted with tracks. Similar bogies were used on some transporter trailers for machine gun carriers, see page 21. The more elaborate dummy axle with a jib and hand operated winch, mentioned on page 15, was carried on two pneumatic tyred wheels. This was in use during the 1930s and enabled any suitable towing vehicle to recover a casualty by suspended tow.

*Dummy axle with jib and hand operated winch dating from the early 1930s.*

# Chapter 4
# Tank Recovery and the First Tank Transporters

Tank recovery in World War I has been described in Part 1. Railways were then the only means of carrying tanks over long distances. In the first few years of the inter-war period rapid developments were taking place in motor transport. Paradoxically, as the size and power of motor lorries developed, tank weights reduced, the 30-ton heavy tanks of World War I giving way to the 12-ton Vickers Mediums. In spite of improved steel for track shoes and less weight, the higher speeds offered by the new designs caused excessive track wear. For a few years instead of looking to the motor industry for transporters a great deal of design effort was diverted to wheel-cum-track vehicles, which used wheels for strategic moves and tracks for combat. The wheels were raised and lowered mechanically and the resulting complex arrangements served only to show that an ideal solution is rarely practical. A clear disadvantage of the wheel-cum-track concept was that it was of no help in recovery. A tank with a siezed engine, for example, could not be moved without the use of another vehicle. Between 1926 and 1931 Vickers produced various wheel-cum-track designs including a variant of their current medium tank.

Peacetime training took place on well-defined training areas mostly with rail access and caused few problems for tank transport and recovery as time was rarely a consideration. It was clear though that if tanks were to make long

approach marches on tracks these would need to be harder wearing. A means of moving disabled tanks was still needed.

In 1919 the RASC acquired a number of articulated low-loaders consisting of AEC 4-wheeled tractors, based on the K type lorry but fitted with chain-driven rear axles. The conversions and semi-trailers were the work of HC Bauly of London and were intended for carrying Holt artillery tractors. The contemporary Medium C tank was only 7 tons heavier than the Holt and this tractor/semi-trailer combination ought to have indicated the answer to the problem of recovering and carrying disabled tanks. At that time, however, 12 tons was about the maximum that could be carried on such a transporter. By 1926, the time of the General Strike, it was possible to deploy some Vickers tanks using commercial transporters. One was demonstrated to War Office staff at about this time at Chelsea Barracks.

In 1928 one of the AEC Bauly vehicles still in use was tested carrying a Vickers Medium Tank. The transporter was found to be too slow, being underpowered and quite unsuitable for off-road use. A year later a Scammell commercial articulated vehicle was tested, again carrying a Vickers Medium. The 8-wheeled lorry comprised a solid tyred 4×2 tractor and a semi-trailer with four solid tyred wheels in line on two stub axles. At that time two Scammell

*Modified AEC K type tractor with Bauly semi-trailer for carrying Holt Caterpillar tractors.*

semi-trailers were available with this wheel arrangement. One was a low-loader and the other a flat-decked platform trailer. Which of these two was used is not recorded. The trials vehicle was not considered ideal but was better than the ancient AEC. By this time even some of the World War I heavy tanks still in use had been transported by civilian contractors using commercial articulated low-loaders of some 25 tons capacity.

The War Office was still more concerned with the recovery problem than with strategic movement. To save money some 'in house' ideas were tried out; thus while modern articulated lorries were being tested two very odd competing designs of tank recovery trailer, tailor-made for the Vickers Medium Tank, were built as prototypes. Both used four traction engine type steel wheels; in the Southern Command pattern the trailer frame supported the weight of the tank from beneath while in the Aldershot Pattern a cranked frame over the tank hull supported a net of steel cables on which the tank was carried. Both designs were archaic, impractical and even unsafe when moving. Despite this, official reports in 1930 and 1932 suggested that the Southern Command pattern was the better of the two and might have been adopted but for two more promising

developments. One of these was the Scammell Pioneer tank transporter which was under development in this period and the other was the possibility of carrying tanks on heavy 6-wheeled commercial lorries.

Drawings of a much better and previously unknown design produced in the Ordnance workshop at Aldershot in 1928 came to light in 1984 in the REME Museum. These show an 8-wheeled recovery tractor with a built-in jib and an 8-wheeled transporter trailer of more conventional design, very advanced for its time, incorporating pneumatic-tyred wheels. The fact that it was not produced may well stem from the likely cost at a time of considerable economies in War Office budgets, and the concurrent emergence of the Scammell Pioneer tractor. There is no indication whether the RAOC drawings were solely a military design study or if a vehicle manufacturer was involved. Both AEC and Guy Motors were at this time developing 8-wheeled cross country vehicles.

The development of the Scammell Pioneer has been described on page 17. To carry tanks the tractor was fitted with a turntable and a semi-trailer with a detachable rear bogie, mounted on four large pneumatic-tyred wheels. Only one of these vehicles was built, WD number H22509

*Southern Command pattern tank recovery trailer, photographed in 1929.*

*The original Scammell 20-ton tank transporter carrying a Medium Dragon artillery tractor, similar to one later modified as a tank recovery vehicle.*

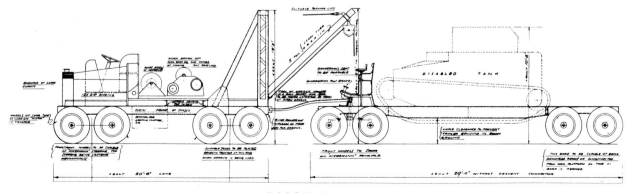

*Breakdown tractor and tank transporter designed in 1928 in the RAOC Workshop Aldershot.*

(civilian registration MV5364). Delivered in 1932, it was photographed in numerous situations throughout southern England in the mid-1930s. It was operated by the RAOC, specifically as a recovery vehicle for use when tanks or similar tracked vehicles could not be towed. The tractor's winch provided a means of 'unsticking' vehicles and loading them, with minimum effort on the part of the crew, except that is for removing and replacing the rear bogie. Using the hand-operated jacks was a tedious business. This first modern tank transporter spent a lot of its time as a training vehicle for Ordnance Corps officers and mechanics.

As part of the rearmament programme in 1937 Scammells were asked to produce an updated transporter. The first eight of these used a longer wheel-base version of the Pioneer gun tractor chassis for the tractor but still used the 20-ton semi-trailer with detachable rear bogie. The need for a better semi-trailer was soon recognised and the second design of 20-tonner, like the 30-tonner, incorporated a fixed rear bogie.

Trials of a Leyland Hippo 6×4 lorry took place over some years from 1931 and, while its use as a tank transporter soon foundered as tanks heavier than the Vickers Medium were designed, it was to become the Army's first heavy cargo lorry.

The Carden and Vickers light tanks and machine-gun carriers, and other light tracked vehicles developed by the then Colonel Giffard Martel, all needed transporters for long moves. The Carden Loyd Company offered its own trailer design with a small bogie on each side fitted with two solid tyred wheels. Each bogie could be fitted with tracks if required. Other trailers were designed by the War Office Design Department, including one 8-wheeler using four bogies similar to ones on the 4-wheeled trailer. Another design widely tested was a 2-wheeled trailer with a low floored trackway between the two wire-spoked wheels. Later, a more robust version was produced by Taskers to a War Office design and featured a 2-wheeled bogie on each side looking rather like the chassis of present-day horse box trailers.

Shortly before World War II Messrs Cranes of Dereham Ltd became involved in the design of trailers for the carriage of light tracked vehicles. One 5-ton capacity design produced in small numbers from 1937 featured a single tubular main frame to which were attached two rear cross members, each supporting two stub axles and a total of eight small wheels. The steerable turntable at the front carried two larger wheels. Twin trackways for the transported vehicle rested on three cross members over the pole-type chassis. Two detachable loading ramps were carried. The suspension of the sets of rear wheels on each side of the trailer was interconnected so that all wheels remained on the ground over rough country, preventing overloading of the tyres. This design led to an improved type produced during 1938, initially for the Indian Army. It features longer trackways and six wheels only with 10.50 × 13 tyres and was rated at 7½-tons capacity. About 1,800 had been built by the end of the war.

Some of the World War I heavy tanks with salvage gear

*Scammell Heavy Breakdown Tractor model SV1S with jib folded and Cranes 7½-ton Light Recovery Trailer c 1940.*

continued in use for a time after that war and for the next twenty years the problem of tank recovery, or, more precisely, what equipment it required, was to exercise minds in the War Office, the RTC and RAOC. Tracked vehicles were still seen as the best means of recovering tanks to a point where they might be repaired or transported to workshops. One scheme was to convert surviving just post-World War I Medium C tanks, but this fell through. Another idea, apparently tried, used a modified 'Medium Dragon' tracked artillery tractor. A Ransomes and Rapier crane was fitted and a hand-operated winch but reports of its trials were somewhat negative and no energy seems to have been applied to solving the apparently minor difficulties described. It is doubtful whether funds would have been granted anyway for new dragons for this role. The vehicle was unarmoured so would have given no protection to its crew.

In the 1930s a RTC company on the North West Frontier of India did convert a Vickers Light tank into a form of ARV but little is known about it. Another scheme would have converted the Army's three 16-ton Vickers Medium Mark III tanks to recovery vehicles, but instead, one at least finished its days as a recovery training hulk at Bovington. Once rearmament began the rush was on to provide as many

*Vickers Light Tank Mark IIB modified as an ARV in India.*

gun tanks as possible, and even if designs had existed it is doubtful if tank hulls would have been made available then for non-combat use.

Many of the trials of commercial load-carrying vehicles for carrying tanks during the inter-war years were aimed at proving their suitability for impressment in the event of war. The War Office saw no reason to invest in large numbers of vehicles to sit in stores awaiting the possibility of mobilisation when they might easily be obtained when needed. As early as 1928 British manufacturers had produced vehicles capable of carrying, on roads at least, any tanks the Army might conceivably ever acquire. In that year Scammells advertised an articulated low loader capable of carrying 25 tons and a year later built their first 100-ton capacity articulated low loader. Also in 1928, the Eagle Engineering Company Ltd produced its first 30– to 50-ton 6-wheeled full trailer. These vehicles would have been slow moving, but by the outbreak of World War II British commercial 8-wheeled lorries were capable of carrying 18 to 20 tons at up to 30 mph in favourable circumstances, although limited by law to 15 tons at 20 mph. Many of these 1930s commercial rigid lorries and tractors with trailers or semi-trailers were to be used during the war, on hire to the War Office or MOS, for moving tanks of up to 40 tons in weight on Britain's roads.

Occasions arise when wheeled vehicles need to be transported. In the early 1930s the War Office took delivery of a 3-ton capacity low-loading lorry designed for this purpose by Garner Motors. It used a 4-wheeled chassis, available commercially for municipal vehicles and was fitted with small pneumatic tyred wheels, twin at the rear. Its front axle was set back under the rear of the cab giving a good weight distribution and a layout which still looks quite modern. A hand winch was used for loading 'dead' vehicles.

Leyland Motors used at least two variants of their pre-war designed Octopus 8×4 rigid lorry during World War II with an extra rear axle, probably unpowered, that is, a 10×4 and an extra wide body for tank carrying. It is believed these were only used for delivering tanks built by the company.

# Part 3
# The Second World War

# Chapter 1
# The Outbreak of War: The Campaign in France and Belgium and its Legacies

Britain's rearmament in the 1930s responded to a recognised threat from a rearming Germany, hence the emphasis on defensive equipment. Britain and France had entered into a treaty to defend Poland if it were attacked. Germany had demonstrated its expansionist plans by annexing Austria followed by part of Czechoslovakia, the latter provoking the journey of Mr Chamberlain, the British Prime Minister, to Munich in 1938. He returned having negotiated a face-saving settlement which effectively gave way to Adolf Hitler, but the military situation in Britain then, with rearmament only just under way, really gave the Prime Minister little choice. Hitler indicated that Germany was now satisfied but few in Britain, despite passionate hope and a loathing for war, expected that peace could be maintained.

In the event of a war, Britain had agreed to send to France an expeditionary force which would comprise, as in World War I, the handful of Regular Army divisions not required to 'police the Empire'. The TA would form a follow-up element for the Regulars. The 13 TA infantry divisions were, theoretically, organised just as the six regular ones and entirely dependent on motor transport, but during a period when Regular Army modernisation was expected to take till 1940, equipment for the TA was woefully inadequate: then, in the 'Munich' crisis, it was decided to double the size of the TA to 26 divisions. This 'stroke of the pen' caused unimaginable logistic problems. Manpower was available but precious little else.

The Army's MT strength had increased sixfold between 1936 and 1939 but this still fell short of the Regular Army's needs. Faced with the TA expansion, further orders were placed for new vehicles from manufacturers including those in Canada, but the short-term answer had to be impressment. The existing plans were scrapped for the commandeering of a selected range of good condition cargo vehicles equating to accepted Army vehicle load capacities: instead, from September 1939, there came into military use a huge variety of vehicles by size, age and manufacture which represented a logistic nightmare. By February 1940 some 35,000 vehicles had been commandeered. The provision of specialist vehicles such as recovery tractors was less easy but some civilian equivalents were requisitioned.

When the war began the independently governed countries of the Empire had all followed Britain's declaration of war on Germany. Even South Africa, whose loyalty was thought suspect by some, quickly came to Britain's aid. The more closely controlled Empire countries such as India and the smaller colonies, perhaps inevitably, offered support. Whilst this provided a huge potential reservoir of manpower, few of the countries were sufficiently industrialised to equip armies without help from Britain, hard pressed then to equip its own.

After Mr Winston Churchill succeeded Mr Neville Chamberlain as Prime Minister the opposition parties joined in a 'National Government' so that the prosecution of the war might take precedence over party considerations. The new leader had launched the landship project when First Lord of the Admiralty in World War I and continued to take a lively interest in military equipment.

As the BEF moved to France and took up positions in the North near the Belgian border, France mobilised its largely Infantry army and trusted to the strength of its fixed defence, the Maginot Line, despite the fact that this was at the time incomplete. Gaps in the line included the Ardennes area which was left poorly guarded since the terrain was considered unsuitable for armoured forces, a decision of the French High Command that was to prove disastrous.

For six months there was relatively little action and fears of instant aerial bombardment of cities, poison gas attacks and massed tank assaults on the allied armies all subsided. This respite enabled factories in the UK to produce considerable numbers of vehicles and so some of the less suitable impressed transport was replaced. Production of tanks, specialist vehicles and weapons involved more complex industrial processes and so lagged behind. Many of the new TA divisions sent to France were, for this reason, little more than a rifle-armed labour force. Despite this, when the Germans eventually attacked in the spring of 1940 through the Ardennes, having first lured the British Army and some French forces north into Belgium, these ill-equipped TA divisions were soon in the front line and suffered accordingly. The German 'blitzkrieg' or lightning war was ably demonstrated in a drive to the French coast which was to isolate all the forces to the north. The only hiccup in the plan was when the one British Army tank brigade in France, a small formation of Matilda infantry tanks, bought time in a counter-attack near Arras and caused some alarm to the German High Command. The invulnerability of these tanks to normal anti-tank weapons was soon ended by the high velocity 88mm AA guns used for the first time against tanks.

As the German advance began Britain hastily dispatched to France the 1st Armoured Division. Ill-equipped, poorly trained and without most of its supporting Arms it went into action immediately on arrival and was decimated. None of the allied armies, British, French or Belgian was able for long to withstand the German onslaught. In general they were all insufficiently trained, led or equipped for a modern war of movement. This, for Britain, was inexcusable after all the trials of mobile forces which had taken place in the 1920s and 1930s and with the country's earlier lead in tank design. Based on its experience in the Spanish Civil War, Germany used its already legendary Army/Airforce cooperation to break up many allied formations which soon became disorganised as they withdrew to the coast. The rescue mission from Dunkirk brought out nearly 400,000 troops but virtually all their vehicles, heavy weapons and equipment were abandoned, much still intact. Most then passed into German use.

Technical support to the BEF had remained disjointed due in part to the pre-war organisation, with repair tradesmen distributed among many corps and regiments. Although the RAOC took many mobile workshops to France and set up a base organisation and static workshops many of its hastily recruited men had little experience of military equipment, even though most were already skilled tradesmen. The dilution of the TA resulted in extreme shortages of workshop and recovery equipment. Potential improvements in the organisation were soon identified and the first independent recovery units were established.

In February 1940 the War Office set up a Tank Repair and Recovery Committee whose chairman was the Director of Ordnance Services (Engineering) (DOS(E)). The vital importance of the logistic support for mechanised armies was at last being recognised. The Committee was to investigate the need for recovery equipment and to set up a trials unit. The precipitous departure from France and the concentration on anti-invasion measures which followed were to delay this project.

The Regular divisions and tank brigades and the few reasonably well equipped TA divisions had, between them, taken to France and left there the bulk of the Army's recovery vehicles. These included the first few production Scammell 20-ton tank transporters and heavy breakdown tractors, some of the surviving AEC R6T breakdown lorries, hundreds of 3-ton gantry lorries and RASC breakdown lorries and some 30-cwt Morris Commercials. In addition, many of the new Cranes light recovery trailers and some earlier Taskers trailers plus a number of impressed civilian recovery vehicles and trailers were lost. The first US Mack and White lorries had been received and converted to tank transporters before the end of the campaign and some reports suggest that a few had been issued to BEF units. Their fate is not known. One Scammell breakdown tractor captured by the Germans at this time was recaptured about three years later in North Africa. Many of the rearmament

period tanks blooded in this campaign did little but demonstrate their ineffectiveness and unreliability, products as they were of hasty and underfunded development and ill-defined operational philosophy.

Soon after the evacuation France sued for peace and was partitioned, the north being occupied by German forces while the south remained under German domination, controlled by a pro-German government led by Marshal Petain in the old town of Vichy. Adding insult to injury, just as France was on the point of surrender Italy declared war on the allies and attacked southern France. More alarming to Britain was the situation in Africa where large Italian forces in the colonies of Libya, Ethiopia and Somaliland threatened British possessions and the Suez Canal. Adding to the gravity of this situation was the large and modern Italian navy which posed a threat to Malta and to passage through the Mediterranean.

In Britain the re-equipping for 'Home Defence' of the returned BEF and those new, former TA, divisions which had remained in the UK now became vital. Of the many priorities the easiest to meet was the restoration of mobility to the Army. Shift-working in the motor industry, despite the setbacks of enemy air raids and the loss of manpower to the armed forces, gradually replaced lost transport but the short term answer was another round of impressment and local purchasing of vehicles. Many buses were acquired at this time as troop transports. The rate of production of new vehicles was hampered by the lack of standardisation between manufacturers. Even had time allowed the design of standard types to be built by different firms this would have been difficult to achieve in the face of commercial rivalry and traditions even in wartime. There was no short-term answer to the slow rate of production of tanks and special vehicles such as tank transporters and recovery vehicles.

Before the war preparatory work had begun to enable the Canadian motor industry to build military vehicles, particularly trucks within the British Army load capacity classes and with certain common features including body styles and tyre sizes. Working closely with the Canadian Defence Department, motor firms produced designs for a range of military trucks which were to be built jointly by the local branches of Ford and General Motors. They differed mainly in the engines and transmission but were of almost identical size and appearance. They became known as the Ford and Chevrolet 'Canadian Military Pattern' (CMP) vehicles. Also in 1939 the War Office sent a Purchasing Commission to the USA to see what suitable vehicles and equipment might be available. France too placed orders for US trucks but the export of other warlike stores was barred by US foreign policy. Britain sought vehicles built to British specifications but US firms were reluctant to embark on such contracts which in any case might never be needed if, as soon seemed likely, the Germans should win. In the desperate situation after the fall of France Britain took up outstanding French contracts and happily purchased off-the-shelf vehicles in the rush to re-equip. The long-term aim of buying specially designed vehicles was, however, pursued. At about this time civilian pattern Canadian trucks were supplied to cover the delays while CMP vehicle production got under way. As Canada sent troops to reinforce Britain, the output of the Canadian factories had initially to be spread more thinly.

Reinforcing the Middle East just when Britain itself was threatened with invasion was an unfortunate necessity and precious stocks of tanks were sent there to enable the Middle East Mobile Division to be modernised. This formation was to become the 7th Armoured Division and formed the backbone of the Western Desert Force which would become the 8th Army.

The Battle of Britain severely discouraged Germany from its Operation SEALION, since, without air superiority and with the Royal Navy largely intact, such a venture was too risky. Germany, having shared Poland with Russia, attacked the USSR, its erstwhile treaty partner, in June 1941. For Britain the threat of invasion still remained but with decreasing probability. A spasmodic continuation of the aerial 'blitz' became a greater danger at home after the centre of land operations had moved to the Middle East and Africa.

The War Office tried in the midst of its many other preoccupations to analyse the lessons of the campaign in France. The reliance on railways for the movement of military formations and especially for tank movement had been a grave mistake in the face of enemy air superiority, especially since Europe had a good road network. Few of the quite logical conclusions drawn from these studies were to have much relevance in North and East Africa.

The pre-war designed Infantry tanks Marks II and III, Matilda and Valentine respectively, were in production by 1940 but only the former had been tested in battle. Matilda was the better armoured and yet proved vulnerable to larger high velocity weapons, suggesting something with even thicker armour was necessary. As part of the extension of tank production to firms previously in other engineering fields, the shipbuilders Harland and Wolff had produced a pilot model of a new heavy tank, the A20, in early 1940. It was essentially a refinement of the basic World War I heavy tank shape but with turret-mounted main armament, and was intended for a similar role should another continental war prove to be as static as the previous one. In the crisis following the Dunkirk evacuation, Vauxhall Motors took over the A20 project and, based on its general shape, designed and planned the production of Infantry Tank Mark IV, the Churchill. With the dire situation in Britain in 1940 it was ordered 'off the drawing board', that is, without extensive prototype testing. Inevitably it quickly developed a reputation for unreliability but successive modifications soon overcame the problems, aided by the fact that for

about a year almost all the Churchill tanks produced remained in Britain and accessible to the manufacturer. To power this vehicle Vauxhall Motors, assisted by some experts from General Motors, the parent company, designed a horizontal 12-cylinder engine consisting essentially of two 6-cylinder engine blocks on either side of a common crankcase. This illustrates the difficulties faced by British tank designers for want of sufficiently powerful engines. Even this expedient resulted in a severely underpowered vehicle capable of little more than 15 mph. In its combat role accompanying infantry this may have been adequate but approach moves on tracks were ponderous, since the speed of a mixed force was geared to the slowest vehicle. Despite some drawbacks the thick armour and consequent weight of the Churchill were to make it a very suitable basis for various special armoured vehicles which were to be developed later.

At this time a number of vehicle manufacturers were asked to produce designs for 4-wheel drive lorries in the 30-cwt and 3-ton classes in recognition of the performance limitations of 2-wheel drive vehicles. Some new 4×4 vehicles were later built with chassis winches giving them a useful light recovery potential.

In the design of recovery vehicles there was little significant progress but among the important developments was the first production version of the Scammell 30-ton tank transporter, followed later by an improved 20-ton version. The time-wasting removable semi-trailer wheels were replaced on the 20-tonner by smaller diameter wheels under the horizontal bed of the semi-trailer. This resulted in a reasonably low and stable vehicle. The 30-tonner had a steeply sloping semi-trailer which, when laden with the high American tanks which it would carry later in the war, could easily foul low bridges. The rear wheels on the tractor were fitted with 15.00 × 20 tyres. The front wheels and the trailer wheels used 13.50 × 20 tyres. Not many years beforehand the prospect of carrying 30-ton loads on pneumatic tyres would have been ridiculed. Both types of transporter had hinged rear ramps and were intended specifically as tank recovery vehicles, there being still no War Office requirement for the strategic movement of tanks by road. This was soon to change. Another Scammell development at this time was the change to the SV2S version of the heavy breakdown tractor. Production of all Scammells was very slow due to their complexity.

The Churchill tank was due to weigh well in excess of 30 tons and its recovery was expected to be beyond the capacity of even the heavier Scammell transporter. With the future A20 in mind manufacturers had been asked to produce trailers capable of carrying a 40-ton tank and these proved eminently suitable for the Churchill.

# Chapter 2
# 1940–1941 The Campaigns in North and East Africa and Contemporary Equipment

Britain and France financed the construction of the Suez Canal and, after Egypt was freed from Turkish domination in World War I, Britain obtained agreement to the stationing of a protective military presence in the Canal Zone. This was to ensure freedom of passage to India and the Far East and, with increasing importance, to the oilfields of Persia and Iraq.

Apart from India, Britain's largest overseas military commitment was the Middle East. Besides the Canal Zone there was a need to police Palestine in the face of growing Arab-Jewish strife. The RAF guarded the oil pipelines in Iraq and garrisoned Aden. Britain supervised the Sudan Defence Force, little more than an internal security force. The Kings African Rifles (KAR), the local regiment in the East African colonies, was also mainly an internal security and ceremonial force. Both, however, had been given some additional funds and modernised to a degree when Italy invaded Ethiopia in the early 1930s.

When France surrendered and Italy entered the war the Middle East situation was bleak for Britain. Its forces had now to contend with the pro-Vichy French forces in Syria-Lebanon and the threat to the Suez Canal traffic posed by Italians in Libya and the Italian colonies bordering the Red Sea. There was a fear too that Turkey might enter the war allied to Germany as in World War I. Despite the threat of invasion Britain had to send reinforcements, others coming from India, Australia and New Zealand. A build up of the Canal Zone base began and this would eventually include four base workshops, originally RAOC then later REME. These and one each in Palestine and Iraq between them were to provide a huge repair and manufacturing resource for the armies operating all over the Middle East, East Africa and the Mediterranean area.

In 1940 the 7th Armoured Division, the Desert Rats, led the carefully prepared but daring campaign which had temporarily eliminated the Italian threat to Egypt by February 1941. Before the whole of Libya could be occupied reinforcements had to be sent to Greece where the Germans had intervened to help a faltering Italian invasion. The German air and tank superiority soon caused the evacuation of the allied troops from Greece to nearby Crete and then from Crete itself. In each case there were severe losses of men and equipment. Further reinforcements were continuously provided for the Army in North Africa but few reached the thinly held front-line before the fresh

German forces under General Erwin Rommel, with new Italian reinforcements, took the initiative in March 1941.

The handful of Vickers light tanks, worn-out cruisers and some new and untried Empire troops were no match for this revitalised enemy. Many of the British Army's tanks were undergoing long-overdue repairs and overhauls and so desperate was the situation that one tank regiment was in the process of re-equipping with captured Italian tanks when Rommel launched his attack.

Allied transport at this time comprised a mixture of pre-war British types and US and Canadian commercial vehicles, some purchased from dealers in Egypt. By mid-1941 the first Canadian 4-wheel drive vehicles began to arrive. Liberal use was made of captured Italian transport, which was well designed, robust and highly regarded. Two new types of tank began to reach the desert from Britain later in 1941, the Infantry Tank Mark III, the Valentine and the Cruiser tank Mark VI, the Crusader.

North Africa consists of a wide variety of soils and surfaces. Inhabited areas have cultivated fields, but the desert itself includes firm sandy soil sometimes with rocky outcrops, soft sand, areas of hard level ground strewn with loose boulders, marsh and rocky areas often divided by deep wadis (dried-up river beds) sometimes hundreds of feet below the level of surrounding land. There are also mountainous areas. The ability of wheeled recovery vehicles to deal with tank recovery tasks in the early days was limited by the shifting variety of the terrain. In soft sand or marshy ground the recovery vehicles themselves were liable to become casualties and a tractor was needed that could operate successfully on soft ground.

The RAOC LADs were responsible together with their parent armoured regiments for tank recovery. Other LADs and, in the RASC companies, the unit workshop platoons dealt with B vehicles. The back-up was largely provided by recovery vehicles from the Ordnance mobile workshops. The huge distances over which formations moved and consequent journey times soon led to the creation of additional logistic units to cover the L of C leading back to the Canal Zone base. One such unit, an L of C recovery Section, was to grow into the 8th Army Recovery Company. When the battles moved forward its tasks included recovering vehicles left behind as the front-line recovery teams moved forward.

In addition to the extrication of damaged or bogged tanks

from the place where they came to grief, there was a need to carry those which could not be towed, in any case a difficult task with tracked vehicles. The usual means of towing tanks was by steel wire ropes (cables) or by chains. Steering an unpowered tank while under tow was sometimes virtually impossible. Ropes and chains broke and some luckless crewman had to dismount and try to reconnect the vehicles, a feat of some heroism when under fire. Despite these problems many successful recoveries were made.

*Impression of the AEC Matador modified to recovery vehicle by 3rd Hussars LAD RAOC in 1941.*

There were in Egypt at the start of the campaign only a few RAOC(E) Leyland breakdown gantry lorries and one 20-ton tank transporter. RASC units had their own complement of recovery vehicles. Much effort went into acquiring extra equipment. Maximum use was made of suitable captured Italian lorries, the potential of Italian gun tractors for recovery use being discovered early in the battle. The steady trickle of new recovery vehicles from the UK was augmented by local conversions and by the widespread use of AEC Matador gun tractors. These were issued to tank regiment LADs, brigade workshops and were even used to pull the US commercial heavy trailers pressed into service then as tank transporters. The bulky outline of the Matador, like the 3-ton gantry lorry, was an embarrassment in the front line. Lieutenant (later Brigadier) G.W.H. Fellows RAOC, who commanded the 3rd Hussars LAD, pioneered a Matador modification. The cab top was removed and the body replaced by a lighter body from a 15-cwt truck. A crane was fitted using an 'I' beam jib and a winch from a wrecked Italian gun tractor. The modified Matador was a much lower and less conspicuous vehicle. The prototype served in the Tobruk bridgehead and drawings of the vehicle were circulated to enable other examples to be built. One of these original drawings survives in the REME Museum. Some Matadors were fitted with Weaver-type cranes and others with a local design

*Lorry 3-ton 4×4 Canadian Ford F60 modified to recovery vehicle in Egypt. Manual jib winch. Sand tyres fitted.*

similar to that on the FWD R6T. Some Canadian Ford F60 3-ton 4×4 lorries were also modified into recovery vehicles.

The L of C Recovery Section was equipped solely through local purchase. In 1939 Brigadier W.W. Richards, Director of Ordnance Services at Headquarters Middle East Command, discovered a fleet of US Marmon Herrington 6×6 oilfield lorries belonging to the South Mediterranean Oil Company. These were purchased, stripped of their superstructures and converted to recovery vehicles. Nearly three years later the jib from one of these was transferred to an AEC Matador which had been found abandoned in the desert by 69 Infantry Brigade Workshop. The shortage of recovery vehicles for use in the Canal Zone was equally desperate. Some obsolete Morris Commercial Leader lorries were converted to breakdown vehicles and also some Chevrolets. As the build-up of equipment progressed some

*Canadian Ford 3-ton 4×2 truck with Holmes Wrecker gear.*

*AEC Matador modified into armoured breakdown vehicle at 4 Base Workshop RAOC in 1941.*

more British 6×4 gantry bodied 3-tonners and an increasing number of Scammells arrived.

The first new design recovery vehicles to reach the 8th Army were based on Canadian civilian pattern trucks with minor modifications. These were the Ford ECO 98T and Chevrolet 15-43X2. Both carried Holmes recovery equipment but had no main chassis winch. During the 1920s the ever expanding use of motor vehicles in the USA spawned thousands of garages or 'gas stations', most of which put together some form of breakdown vehicle. One garage proprietor, Ernest Holmes, built the first 'twin boom wrecker' with two swinging jibs which, linked together, could lift heavy vehicles at the rear or, singly, a lighter vehicle at either side. Similar designs were produced by Gar Wood Industries and many US and Canadian recovery vehicles were to be fitted with this form of lifting gear.

The gantry body, seen mostly on the Leyland Retriever 6×4 chassis at this time, was adopted by other Empire armies. The Australians used a version of it on 3-ton 4-wheeled Ford, Chevrolet and International chassis as well as on some 6-wheeled chassis. In 1941 another AEC Matador variant was produced in the Canal Zone workshops. This was fitted with an armoured cab, Canadian-built steel truck body and girder crane. It is recorded that the British Ordnance officer with the Free French Brigade requested that this vehicle be issued to his workshop but was refused it.

The US development of the Holt tractor before World War I led to a range of tracked tractors, available from various manufacturers and in many sizes. They were intended for agricultural and construction site work and, in 1940, some Caterpillar D8 tractors of massive proportions and considerable power were purchased for the RE. In North Africa, where the limitations of wheeled recovery vehicles were soon obvious, some D8s were issued to RAOC(E) for tank recovery. Later, smaller D7 and D4 tractors were used in this role, together with the International TD18 and other makes. The larger tractors were very capable recovery vehicles once fitted with suitable winches. The Caterpillar versions remained in use long after the war. The tractor's drawback was lack of speed so that it could only be moved to recovery sites on a trailer. At first commercially designed American trailers were used. When the tractor had winched or pulled a vehicle casualty onto solid ground a second recovery tractor or transporter was needed to move it, as the first usually pulled the D8's own trailer. Despite this, and the other severe limitation shared with wheeled recovery vehicles – no armour protection – the tractors were unrivalled for tank recovery in soft ground. The Caterpillar D8 weighed about 17 tons. Different winches were fitted, some having capacities of up to 45 tons.

After the German Army became involved in the campaign some half-tracks were captured. The larger versions of these were extremely practical recovery vehicles and were used whenever possible.

Tank recovery, as in France, remained the province of unarmoured wheeled recovery tractors and lorries (the

*German Famo 18-ton half track used by RAOC as a tank recovery vehicle. Crusader tank on tow.*

*Mack EXBX 18-ton transporter with Valentine Infantry Tank Mark III. This transporter has the 'bees knees' folding ramps replaced in later models by simple detachable ramps. North Africa November 1941.*

*The Caterpillar D8 tractor towing a Federal 20-ton tank transporter. Photographed after the war in Malaya. These are two of the vehicle types deployed in North Africa in 1942/43.*

*The winch equipped White Ruxtall transporter with Valentine tank fitted with sand shields.*

distinction was one of size) and the few winch-equipped Scammell transporters until the D8 tractors were issued. Early improvisation led to disabled tanks being carried on grossly overloaded 7½-ton light recovery trailers, on commercial trailers, on heavy lorries or being towed by any vehicle heavy enough to tackle the job.

Scammell transporter production remained totally inadequate to meet needs. By April 1941 only fifteen of the 30-ton variant had been built and many of these remained in the UK for trials and training. Less than 500 were to be produced in total by the end of the war. Further supplies of the Mack and White transporters ordered in 1940 became available when Britain took over the French contracts after the fall of France. Many of these vehicles were required in the UK for home-defence forces and in any case it took time to build the transporter bodies and to ship completed vehicles to the Middle East. Of three available types, Mack EXBX, White Model 920 and White Ruxtall, only the latter was really suited to recovery as it alone was fitted with a winch. The method adopted for loading disabled tanks on to the Mack and White was for a cable to be attached to each

side of the front of the tank. The cables were run up over guides or pulleys on the side of the transporter and attached to two lorries stationed to the front of it. When the lorries drove forward the tank was drawn up on to the transporter. The process took at least fifteen minutes, was wasteful of equipment and very difficult on uneven terrain. Nonetheless, these methods were necessary in the absence of sufficient purpose-built recovery transporters. Later in the campaign, when heavier transporters became available, some Macks and Whites were rebodied as cargo vehicles.

A coastal railway line leading from the Canal Zone to the Egyptian town of Mersa Matruh was used to move new and, later, reconditioned tanks forward to the border defence area, as the earlier experience of the Western Desert Force and the extensive training undertaken before the attack on the Italians had shown up the problem of rapid track wear in the desert. When the battles moved further west, beyond the railway, the War Office was advised by Headquarters Middle East Command of the need for transporters for the strategic movement of tanks.

Earlier, in September 1940, three months after Dunkirk,

the idea of using transporters to save track wear and driver fatigue was discussed in the War Office. As a result the White Model 920 was tested in this role in Britain but was considered unsuitable. Nothing much was achieved then apart from identifying a need for transporters in the UK where railways did not reach some tank unit locations and new training areas. Later MOS was asked to produce designs for transporters and this was given some urgency when the demands for these vehicles came from the Middle East.

While the War Office and MOS procedures creaked into action, the immediate Middle East requirements were met by sending out Mack 10-ton 6×4 Model NR lorries, standard American commercial types purchased previously as cargo vehicles and held in Ordnance depots. The Macks were fitted with simple transporter bodies with detachable loading ramps. Being smaller than the Mack EXBX the NRs were rated at 13-tons capacity but in service were frequently overloaded. These, together with a handful of Mack EXBX and White 920s equipped the early RASC tank transporter companies, the first of which became operational in November 1941. When later supplanted by larger transporters some of each type were handed over to the RAOC to increase its numbers of recovery transporters.

In 1940 an Italian invasion of British Somaliland was resisted by British and Empire troops. The Italian forces were largely locally recruited but were not defeated until May 1941. The terrain comprised desert and mountainous areas with few roads and was as hard on vehicles as the North African desert. British forces used tanks and the South African Army, the first of its locally built Marmon Herrington armoured cars. Transport was the contemporary mixture of types as used in the Western Desert. Some early CMP trucks reached the area before the East African campaign ended. Here as elsewhere, captured Italian vehicles were put to good use. Recovery vehicles were scarce and much improvisation was called for. The mountainous areas necessitated the use of pack animals and teams of these were sometimes used to recover vehicles. Squads of soldiers or local bystanders were often employed instead.

The two campaigns on the African continent, both carried out in hostile climates and on terrain most unsuitable for the bulk of the vehicles provided for the Army, served to reinforce the RAOC predictions about the need for better equipment and more technical support resources. From mid 1941 the East African theatre became something of a backwater save for the brief build up for the attack on Madagascar in 1942 to take the island from the Vichy French. After this the main task was the policing of the former Italian colonies. Equipment used was mostly civilian pattern Canadian or US trucks, a few Bren Carriers and later some obsolescent light tanks. For these some locally built transporters were used comprising Ford Marmon Herrington 6-wheeled trucks with timber trackways and detachable ramps. Another local improvisation was a Ford 3-tonner fitted with the US M7 recovery equipment more normally found on the GMC 6×6 truck.

*Ford Marmon Herrington 6×4 transporters used in East Africa for moving Bren Carriers and Light tanks.*

# Chapter 3
# 1941–1942 New Organisations and New Equipment

While the Empire armies fought in North and East Africa the steady build-up of Home Forces continued. With a diminished threat of invasion after 1941, the expanding army with, already, a strong contingent from Canada, was now formed into a huge training organisation. Reinforcements were continually being sent overseas but the emphasis for Home Forces gradually changed from defence of the British Isles to preparation for an eventual attack on mainland Europe.

There were still desperate equipment shortages but gradually home output and purchases from the USA and Canada began to cover most needs for general transport. Heavy weapons and particularly tanks could not be acquired elsewhere at first and the construction of some untried and poorly designed armoured vehicles was continued on the pretext that to interrupt production while factories were adapted to build new types would deprive the Army of too many tanks. In retrospect this proved a doubtful argument since so many of the early types of tank were unsound and, in action, were soon lost to the Army anyway because of their inadequacies. Britain's industrial capacity at this time was prodigious but not enough to cope alone with arming the Empire on land, in the air and at sea whilst at the same time manning the armed forces, merchant navy and civil defence organisations. Increasingly therefore dependence had to be placed on imported equipment.

The War Office during this period was reorganised to cope with the expanding Army and in order to develop its technical infrastructure. This was needed to draw up equipment requirements, to liaise with the MOS over design and to carry out troop testing of prototypes. The MEE at Farnborough had passed to the MOS on its formation in 1939. By 1942 a separate MOS testing establishment for fighting vehicles was established at Chertsey and the two organisations became the Wheeled Vehicle Experimental Establishment (WVEE) and the Fighting Vehicle Proving Establishment (FVPE) respectively.

The original Purchasing Commission sent to the USA had arranged production of some vehicles to British specifications and invested considerable sums of money which enabled some US factories to be expanded long before America became directly involved in the war. The US policy of not selling weapons to belligerents was circum-

vented in diverse ways and in 1941 President Roosevelt persuaded Congress to enact a law which, in theory, aimed to combine US and British military output, apportioning to each that which it needed. At the time it would operate much in Britain's favour. Britain leased defence bases in some colonies to the USA in return for hardware. The new system was known as Lend-Lease and all equipment supplied to Britain under the scheme remained, technically, US property. From this time a much larger military liaison staff was established in Washington, taking over the Purchasing Commission's role.

A number of factors in 1941 caused the concept of a separate repair Corps for the Army to be re-examined. The very poor performance of British armour in North Africa and the losses during withdrawals of repairable tanks led to questions in Parliament. The RAOC came in for some unjustified criticism when its efforts were compared by self-appointed 'experts' with those of the German repair organisations. Significant factors poorly understood by those not involved were the ease of recovery when in possession of the battlefield after the enemy had withdrawn, then more often an advantage to the Germans: also, for security reasons, the public was not informed about the inefficiency of some British tanks nor the scarcity of spare parts, repair resources and recovery vehicles.

At the same time a growing shortage of skilled manpower was beginning to affect munitions production. Many trained engineers and tradesmen who had volunteered for or been conscripted into the Army were not being employed where their skills could be best used. There were Army tradesmen in different regiments and corps under the pre-war organisation. In 1941 a Ministry of Labour committee under Sir William Beveridge drew attention to the Army's inefficient employment of skilled labour. Subsequent War Office committees led to the creation of the new Corps, REME, which came into being in October 1942.

The first American tank received in quantity under the Lend-Lease scheme was the Light Tank M3, given the British name General Stuart but often known as the Honey. Weighing 12 tons it was fast but thinly armoured. It was, however, reliable and was slotted into the British tank categories as a light cruiser. It was followed soon by the M3 Medium Tank named the General Lee, another version of it with a British designed turret being the General Grant. US

Tanks were, like contemporary British ones, rear engined but their drive sprockets were at the front with a drive shaft running forward under the turret to the transmission and steering unit. This layout resulted in a much higher tank. In the M3 the 75mm main gun was mounted in a sponson on the right side of the hull. The turret mounted a smaller gun, a 37mm, and a machine gun. The M3 Medium weighed 28 tons and thus added to the difficulties of the recovery organisation. It was a very welcome addition to the 8th Army's fighting strength nonetheless.

After Lend-Lease began Britain continued for a time to obtain equipment of non-standard US Army pattern by direct purchase. There remained a great reluctance by manufacturers or the US Army to accept British war experiences as guidelines for equipment design, for spare parts quantity assessments and, in some cases, whole categories of equipment were not considered necessary. These views often changed as the US Army gained the same experience the hard way.

When at the end of 1940 the War Office began considering tank transporters for more than just recovery it was hoped that some suitable vehicles might be obtainable from British manufacturers. At this time tanks in service or under development weighed from 6 tons to nearly 40 tons, the majority being in the 20- to 25-ton class. The War Office bracketed together 18 to 25 tons allowing for the US 18-ton transporters then being built. The 40-ton capacity covered the Churchill and, fortuitously, most other tanks that were to see service before the war ended. The system of vehicle taxation in Britain before the war had penalised large and powerful engines so the motor industry tried to squeeze the most out of smaller engines by the use of low gears. Firms were thus dissuaded from developing the type of large engines which might prove suitable for tanks weighing more than about 25 tons or for the vehicles which might carry them. Whilst the Scammell's Gardner diesel could cope with a laden 30-ton transporter it was good for only about 15 mph. The Churchill could be carried but at reduced

speed and with a great strain on the vehicle.

The MOS, in seeking increased British production of recovery transporters, had ordered from Albion Motors of Glasgow a 20-tonner. The tractor for this, the CX 24S, was closely based on the firm's 10-ton cargo lorry, the CX23. The semi-trailer bed was nearly horizontal and was carried on two axles whose wheels were fitted with 36×8 tyres giving it a reasonably low loading height. Folding ramps at the rear allowed tanks to be driven or winched on board using the tractor's 8-ton Scammell winch. When the need for more transporters arose in 1941 MOS ordered over 800 of these vehicles even though they could only carry the lighter tanks currently in service. The scale of this order was to prove unwise.

In 1941 MOS negotiated with US manufacturers to obtain the necessary 40-ton transporters. The Purchasing Commission found various truck makers could offer massive vehicles virtually off the shelf but many favoured the tractor semi-trailer combination which the MOS, with experience of the height restriction on the Scammell, sought to avoid for this largest category transporter. The alternative, tractor and full trailer, proposed by US manufacturers was also rejected since the designs were based on commercial earth-moving plant carriers. A form of low loader or drop-frame trailer with swan neck over the front-axle turntable was offered by both the Fruehauf Trailer Company and Rogers Brothers. In this design the tank would be carried on a low bed between the axles which, whilst giving good stability, lacked ground clearance and resulted in a very long vehicle whose turning circle would restrict its use on roads in Britain. At this time the expected main role for transporters was the movement of new tanks in the UK but the proposed trailers would have been useful if not ideal in North Africa and might have been available there sooner.

As part of the 'buy British' policy MOS sought design studies and a quarter-size model of a 40-ton transporter trailer from Scammell Lorries Ltd in October 1940, and two months later from Cranes of Dereham Ltd. A full-size prototype of the Cranes design was available for demon-

*Albion CX24S 20-ton tank transporter.*

stration at MEE on 30 April 1941 to MOS and War Office representatives and two Pickfords heavy-haulage experts whose knowledge was considered valuable.

The design featured a main frame carrying two parallel channel section track-ways which sloped down at the rear and were fitted with folding ramps. Below the frame's cross members at the front a turntable carried two articulated and sprung stub axles in line, each fitted with two twin wheels. Two such lines of stub axles were fitted at the rear on walking beams giving the appearance of a normal three axle trailer. The rear wheels were unsprung. All 24 tyres were 36×8s, a common commercial vehicle size at the time. The channel section track-ways resulted in lips at the outside edge of the trailer which limited its use in its original form to tanks with a width over tracks of about 9½ feet. The trailer was put into production under the War Office designation Trailer Tank Transporter 40-ton Mark I. Licensed production by other firms, notably Dyson, soon followed. After the Cranes trailer was demonstrated the design was offered to US manufacturers for production in place of the overlong designs they had offered.

Rogers Brothers adapted the Cranes design and produced a similar trailer which, due to the use of smaller wheels and 8.25×15 tyres, was slightly lower. In the US design the trackways were not carried so far forward as on the British design and the absence of a lip on the outside edge enabled wider tanks to be carried with their tracks overhanging the trailer. As with the original British design, production was licensed to other manufacturers including Pointer-Willamette, Checker Cab, Winter-Weiss and Fruehauf. All versions in British use were known as Rogers trailers.

The 40-ton trailers were originally conceived as transporters and it was intended that tanks should be driven on, but some were bid for as recovery trailers to make up for the slow production of Scammells. In a sensible effort at standardisation most British trailers were retained in Britain and US trailers were sent to the Middle East. One British 40-ton trailer was, however, used in a Canal Zone depot as the chassis for a massive girder crane. In March 1942 the War Office dropped the tank design criterion which had limited width to enable transport within the British standard railway loading gauge. This was to mean that some tanks designed thereafter could only be carried in Britain by road, thus increasing the need for transporters.

Further trailer development in this period resulted in the Trailer Tank Transporter 40-ton Mark II. This was designed by R.A. Dyson and was of welded construction, very similar in concept and size to the Cranes-designed Mark I but lacking the lip on the edges of the track-ways. It could thus carry wider tanks when necessary. Among the sub-contractors for British 40-ton trailers was the municipal vehicle builder, Shelvoke and Drewry.

Another Cranes design was an off-road 40-ton trailer. This complex vehicle comprised a three-section main frame, each section being hinged to the next so that the articulation would take up any unevenness in the ground. Two rows of wheels were fitted to each section and all were steered using an Ackerman system rather than turntables. The machine was successfully tested but deemed too complicated for Army use.

Heavy tractors for the Rogers trailer were offered by a number of US firms, in some cases based on chassis already in production or ordered for the British Army. They included a heavier version of the Mack LMSW, a White Model 922 and a Ward La France. The vehicle eventually selected was the Diamond T Model 980, a ballast-bodied 6×4 tractor with a long bonnet housing a Hercules diesel engine. Early models featured an all-steel cab but later production including the second version, Model 981, used a folding canvas topped cab to reduce the height for shipping. Paradoxically the 'soft top' versions were mainly available in time for the cold climate of the North-West Europe campaign while the steel-cabbed 980s were like mobile

*The Cranes 40-ton transporter trailer showing clearly the outer lip on the track-ways.*

*Cranes 40-ton articulated transporter showing its remarkable cross-country mobility. The load is a Churchill tank.*

ovens in the North African desert. The important feature of the Diamond T was a transverse mounted winch behind the cab. Rated at 20(US) tons (40,000 pounds), it enabled the tractor to winch disabled tanks on to the trailer. On the Model 981 fairleads were fitted and an aperture cut in the front bumper so that the vehicle could winch forward at a lower capacity. This was intended for self recovery. When the Diamond T was later taken into use by the US Army it was given the designation M20 and, with the Rogers trailer M9, the combination was known as the M19. Because some 40-ton trailers were being built in Britain more tractors were sought than trailers. The totals, ordered in 1941, were 485 tractors, 285 Rogers trailers and 200 British trailers. As the war progressed the British Army was to employ well in excess of a thousand Diamond T tractors with various trailers. When deliveries began in early 1942 transporters were mainly allocated to RASC companies but some went to the RAOC who fitted the trailers with a set of snatch blocks (pulleys) and cable to step up the winching capacity of the tractor when recovering heavier tanks. The imbalance of tractor and trailer shipments to the Middle East resulted in some Rogers trailers being pulled by the adaptable AEC Matador.

Orders for two designs of wheeled recovery vehicle had been placed by the Purchasing Commission in the USA to meet purely British requirements. The Heavy Breakdown Tractor was virtually an Americanised Scammell. Using the petrol-engined Mack LMSW chassis with 14.00×20 tyres on single wheels, this vehicle was fitted with a main winch and a steel body with equipment lockers on either side of a Gar Wood sliding two section jib. This had a power-operated winch. The Canadian Army used this chassis with swinging twin-boom recovery gear and some of this version came into use with REME later in the war. The second UK specification vehicle was intended to supplement the British chassis available for the standard 3-ton gantry body. A US Dodge Model WK60 6×4 chassis was used and featured a semi-forward control layout. The Thornton double-drive rear bogie was a simpler arrangement than the WD type. A Gar Wood chassis winch was fitted but the bodies were British built and identical to those on British chassis. By the end of 1942 both the Mack and Dodge were in use in Britain and the Middle East.

New Canadian recovery vehicles began to reach the British Army in late 1941. The Chevrolet and Ford CMP range included a number of recovery versions on both 30-cwt and 3-ton 4×4 chassis. Some used Holmes wrecker gear and others the similar Gar Wood installation. The essential difference was in the shape of the lifting booms

*The definitive tank transporter. Diamond T tractors with Rogers trailers photographed in Palestine shortly after World War II.*

*Mack LMSW Heavy Breakdown Tractor during a recovery demonstration before the Director of Mechanical Engineering, Major General Rowcroft c 1943.*

*A 'crock train' towed by a Dodge WK 60 gantry lorry. All vehicles in the train apart from the trailer are captured Italian or German trucks.*

which in the Holmes version were tubular, braced with steel rods, whilst the Gar Wood used booms consisting of two parallel girders cross-braced with a lattice of steel strips. Both long and short wheelbase CMP vehicles carried these wrecker bodies. There were also 6-wheeled versions of the CMP range. The Ford F60H was an extended F60 4×4 with an added undriven rear axle. One version of this chassis carried the standard 3-ton gantry body; another used the standard light wrecker body with Holmes gear.

When Lend-Lease came into operation, Britain was under great pressure to accept standard US Army type vehicles which included many features not favoured by the MOS and War Office. Notable among these were twin rear tyres which, although they could often support more weight, tended to trap mud and stones between them and caused problems if the inner tyres were punctured. None of the winches on American-designed tractors was fitted with paying-on gear so the cables were wound on in a criss-cross jumble, causing extra wear and crushing under load, with the result that cables often snapped in use, sometimes with fatal results to recovery crews.

The entry of Japan into the war against Britain and the USA in December 1941 had a number of effects on the supply of equipment from the USA. The need for the USA to mobilise for the first time a fully mechanised army prompted a sudden and massive call on the output from its factories: Britain and the Empire were then no longer the main beneficiary of Lend-Lease but had to take a turn in the queue. It did however bring the USA into the war against Germany and in recognition of the immediate dangers the USA assigned to Britain in 1942 most of its new M4 medium tanks, named by Britain the General Sherman. From Alamein onwards the Sherman increasingly became the main tank of British armoured regiments apart from the Army Tank Brigades which used the Churchill.

At the time US forces were being deployed in Britain with standard US Army recovery vehicles, some of the same types were beginning to reach Britain and the Middle East as Lend-Lease issues. These included the Ward La France M1 and Diamond T Model 969 'wreckers'. The most powerful US recovery vehicle to enter British service, in 1943, was the Ward La France Heavy Wrecker 6×6 M1. It was powered by an 8.2-litre petrol engine and was built with an all steel cab. The main lifting gear was a single swinging boom and three winches were fitted. These were a 20(US)-ton main winch at the rear, a 13(US)-ton front-mounted self-recovery winch and a jib winch with a lifting capacity of 9 tons.

The Diamond T 6×6 Model 969 used a chassis conservatively rated as a 4-tonner by the US Army, but it was a far more powerful vehicle than any British 3-tonner. The Diamond T wrecker chassis was a 'small brother' to the tank transporter tractor with some common components. Its lifting gear, of the Holmes twin-boom type, was already familiar from the smaller Canadian vehicles similarly equipped. It was powered by a petrol engine and fitted with a front mounted 7(US)-ton winch. Early versions were fitted

*Standard US Army issue Truck 4-ton 6×6 Diamond T Model 969 Wrecker showing the two booms being used independently.*

with steel closed cabs but, like most US trucks, the later 969s had soft-top cabs.

During this period there were many recovery equipment developments in the Middle East. The base workshops continued to build improvised recovery vehicles, including a run of AEC Matadors fitted with jibs taken from American built Hyster workshop cranes, one of these remaining in service into the 1950s in the Sudan. Another experiment sought to reduce the height of the standard gantry body. A prototype was built with a lowered girder structure reducing the height to that of the 3-ton cargo vehicle. As the 'I' beam could not then be slid forward for travelling since it would intrude into the cab space, it was instead cut at the rear and hinged so that it folded over on itself above the body roof line. As far as is known no further production of the modified gantry lorry took place.

As a result of the great fund of recovery experience in North Africa, Headquarters Middle East Command sought from the War Office in 1943 an armoured recovery vehicle. In the meantime the headquarters authorised local trials

*Guy FBAX 3-ton breakdown gantry with experimental low height body and rear of jib folded over canopy rails.*

One of a batch of AEC Matadors fitted with US Hyster industrial crane jibs.

A Diamond T photographed in East Africa in 1949. It is fitted with a recovery jib made from pieces of rail line and had been modified previously in the Middle East.

with a US M3 light tank. Documents in the REME Museum record that it coped as a tank tug with tanks of greater weight but at the expense of considerable clutch wear. No major modifications were apparently made to the gun tank for these trials and no production Stuart ARV resulted.

The Albion 20-ton tank transporters proved unable to cope with the rough terrain in North Africa and were de-rated to 15-tons capacity, later being used as heavy cargo vehicles. An alternative transporter, ordered from the USA, came into use later in 1942. This comprised a Federal Model 604 6-wheeled tractor with a Cummins diesel engine and a Trailmobile 20-ton dropframe semi-trailer. A robust and reliable vehicle, it proved to be of only marginal use in its intended role since, by the time of its arrival, most new tanks were the US-built M3s and M4s weighing approximately 30 tons. The 8th Army Recovery Company was quick to question the vehicle's usefulness but designed a modification by fitting a redundant 15-cwt truck body over the trailer's swan neck to carry recovery gear. Later Federal transporters were supplied with purpose-built lockers.

As the numbers of Diamond T transporters increased some problems arose over their employment. The issue of new or reconditioned tanks was an RAOC function though, later, the RAC Armoured Replacement Group took over responsibility for their transit from RAOC depots into the hands of tank units. In North Africa, beyond the railhead, this also involved the RASC tank transporter units. Backloading, like recovery, was an RAOC (later REME) responsibility but there were insufficient transporters for all these tasks to be carried out by each corps in isolation.

Eventually better coordination was achieved to maximise the use of available vehicles, thus transporters returning after a tank delivery run could backload casualties to the Canal Zone workshops for repair. Additional sets of 5-part tackle were provided to enable all tractors to winch 'dead' tanks on to trailers and, when available, RASC transporters assisted with recovery as well as backloading.

REME used the Diamond T for tank recovery alongside the Scammell. Whilst the latter had a better cross-country performance due to its large, low-pressure tyres, it could not easily be separated from its semi-trailer, whereas the Diamond T could more easily leave its full trailer, move off, winch a tank into line with the rear of the trailer then reposition itself at the front of the trailer to winch the casualty on board. This flexibility was a bonus and to further improve their use as recovery vehicles the officer commanding 8th Army Recovery Company, Major Peter Whiteley, proposed that half of the stock of Diamond T tractors should have recovery jibs fitted into their ballast bodies. He had arranged such a conversion using the jib from a wrecked Scammell. Many Diamond T tractors were similarly modified in North Africa and later in Italy. Another experiment, aimed at improving the Diamond T's off-road capability, involved the design of overall tracks for the rear wheels as had long been provided for the Scammell. Tank tracks were used for the Diamond T as their centre guides would fit between the tractor's twin rear tyres. To give clearance for these tracks the ballast bodies on some tractors were raised a few inches by inserting steel girders between the body and chassis.

# Chapter 4
# 1941–1943 The Continued War in the Middle East and North Africa

Following the defeat of the Italian Army in Libya at the battle of Beda Fomm in February 1941 the allied armies, depleted by the reinforcements sent to Greece and Iraq, desperately needed a breathing space to carry out essential maintenance to their battle-worn equipment. As most tanks were withdrawn for overhaul the newly arrived German forces (which would eventually become the Afrika Korps), together with fresh Italian troops, struck at British positions in March 1941. The withdrawal of British and allied troops left a sizeable contingent, mainly Australian, marooned at Tobruk. This force, supplied by sea, remained cut off but fully operational for many months. Further increases in manpower and material enabled the allies to counter-attack and the Germans and their allies were driven back beyond Benghazi allowing the Tobruk garrison to break out. This series of battles to and fro across the desert in which British generalship, equipment and logistic support all came in for criticism, ended with a new German offensive and another allied retreat began in mid-1942.

The expansionist policy of Japan led late in 1941 to the withdrawal of some British units to reinforce the Army in Burma. Other formations which might have favourably influenced the desert war had instead to be sent to Singapore. Later it became necessary to return Australian troops to the Far East to meet the new threat.

This period saw little improvement in the scale of recovery services, which remained largely as previously organised. Gradually more and better equipment became available but there was never enough. The constant withdrawals were characterised by the sight of 'crock trains', recovery or other large vehicles pulling a long line of disabled vehicles on wheels, trailers or even tracks in an effort to bring them back for repair rather than leave them to be captured or destroyed. Each time a workshop moved its 'work in hand' had to be transported in this way.

Recovery crews had the grisly task of extricating the remains of crews from wrecked tanks sometimes long after they had died, and REME workshops were called upon to design and manufacture disinfecting apparatus which became an additional piece of recovery equipment. When enemy tanks were found, or allied ones which could not be recovered quickly and might fall into enemy hands, it was necessary to destroy them, so recovery crews were also trained in the use of explosives.

The German strategy for conquering the Middle East and depriving Britain of oil supplies had become clear in 1941. Rommel's forces advanced in North Africa and, following Operation BARBAROSSA, strong German forces occupied southern Russia, giving the appearance of a carefully designed pincer movement. Other threats existed. The pro-German Vichy French government controlled the colony of Syria and intelligence suggested it was making its airfields available to German aircraft. In the same year a pro-German government took over in Iraq and attacks were made on British troops in the country. German agents were also at work in Persia, the other main source of oil in the

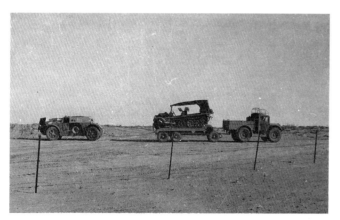

*Captured Italian Spa gun tractor towing Cranes 7½-ton trailer with captured German light half-track and an Italian armoured car.*

*A captured German 23-ton tank transporter trailer Sd Ah 116 carrying a British A9 cruiser tank.*

Middle East. To pre-empt this strategic design Britain formed in 1941 the Persia and Iraq Force (PAIFORCE). Consisting largely of Indian Army formations, PAIFORCE occupied the vacuum of northern Arabia. The dissidents in Iraq and Persia were arrested. Troops of PAIFORCE occupied Iraq and southern Persia whilst the north was policed by Russia. A joint British Empire and Free French force invaded and occupied Syria. From then on with the area secured the main task became one of maintaining routes for British and US war material supplied to Russia, which also began to benefit from 'Lend-Lease'.

The convoy route for supplying Russia ran from Persian Gulf ports across deserts into the mountains in the north of the country and on to the Russian border. A recovery infrastructure was set up but the units lacked sufficient or suitable vehicles. For maximum carrying capacity US 10-ton trucks were mainly used to ferry munitions to Russia, but the only breakdown vehicles available were 3-ton Canadian Fords converted to recovery vehicles by 4 Base Workshop in Egypt. In consequence improvisation became the primary rather than secondary method. Fortunately many US cargo vehicles were fitted with winches. One instance is recorded of a disabled truck being backloaded roped onto the back of another, piggy-back fashion. Later two L of C recovery sections were provided for the area, equipped with a total of 24 heavy recovery vehicles including three Scammells.

After its last retreat the 8th Army finally held off the enemy at the Battle of Alam Halfa which began on the 31 August 1942. By this time the enemy was being starved of supplies and equipment mainly through the success of the RAF and Navy in the Mediterranean. A pause followed this battle during which both sides prepared for the next. The arrival of General Montgomery at this time coincided with a more liberal supply of equipment, much of it Lend-Lease from the USA. His particular genius was to convince 8th Army troops of their ability to win after so many defeats. He placed great emphasis on training and his methods were to be rewarded in the battle of El Alamein in October 1942. Thereafter the enemy was driven out of Egypt and later Libya.

This final push cleared the Western Desert of the enemy, so in early 1943 the way was clear for the unhindered and full-scale recovery of any abandoned vehicles left behind in earlier battles or in the move westwards. The front-line recovery units had to move forward to support the 8th Army and behind the fighting formations there was a huge area containing only supply traffic and small occupation forces in the former Italian towns. To cope with the recovery workload additional units were brought from the Canal Zone, including the Recovery Wing of the REME Middle East School of Instruction, whose students were given practical experience in the desert. Prisoners of War (POWs) were also employed.

An interesting sidelight on the recovery skills and organisation at this time tells of two augmented recovery sections disappearing into the desert and returning nearly two weeks later having recovered over 100 A vehicles, several trucks, 60 POWs and some lost British tank crews. This also demonstrates the cult of independence that some recovery units and individual crews had built up in North Africa. This was founded on the ability to be self-supporting, carrying rations, water, weapons, first-aid supplies, tools and spare parts; and on an unfailing flair for map reading and desert navigation; on training and experience in identifying and dealing with mines and booby traps and in overcoming enemy resistance and, after all this, the skills to carry out the recovery task. Such expertise bred a unique kind of soldier tradesman.

Operation TORCH was conceived with the intention of squeezing Rommel's axis forces between the 8th Army and a newly landed joint British and US group of armies in North Africa. The additional aim was to deny to the axis the resources of the French colonies of Morocco, Algeria and Tunisia and to persuade the French there to renounce the Vichy government and side with General de Gaulle's Free French forces. The operation landed elements of the British 1st Army and a large American force in Algeria. These troops had moved from Britain while another American force, shipped direct from the USA, landed in Morocco. The sites of these landings were dictated partly by the need to provide air cover from Gibraltar. The degree of resistance to be expected from the Vichy French was an unknown quantity.

The hopes of a rapid occupation of Tunisia were frustrated by a rapid German response, poor road communications, terrible weather and inexperience, particularly of US troops at this stage. French resistance to the landings varied but quite soon agreement was reached; the French colonial forces joined the allied armies but outdated equipment and political problems initially blunted their effectiveness. The delays in moving allied forces eastwards gave the enemy plenty of time to reinforce Tunisia bringing troops from France and Italy. In the urge to ship allied fighting troops to Algeria many logistic units were removed from ships at the last minute in Britain, and for a long time REME representation in 1st Army was much too small. The Corps having been formed only just before the ships sailed, units were organised on the new and untried War Office established tables, unlike 8th Army REME units, whose locally approved organisation was the result of two years operational experience. The 1st Army REME units often arrived depleted by those elements relegated to follow-up convoys but were still expected to function as though complete. Early German success, against the Americans particularly, eventually changed to withdrawals as Rommel returned to Germany, and then the 8th Army broke through the Afrika Korps defences on the Libya-Tunisia border and linked up with 1st Army. Despite setbacks the combined allied forces, in due course, drove the Germans and Italians back on Tunis where they surrendered in May 1943.

The vehicles commonly available in Britain in 1942 were allocated to Operation TORCH but there were too few tank transporters with none at first in REME hands capable of carrying the Churchill; this despite the deployment of Churchills with 25th Tank Brigade. Eventually additional 30-ton transporters were sent from the UK. There were however two RASC tank transporter companies equipped with 40-ton transporters. Although transporters were in short supply the notable feature of this operation was the use for the first time of ARVs. Twelve Churchill Mark Is formed part of the Army Tank Brigade and did sterling work but the absence of a winch was a great drawback. The development of ARVs is covered in Chapter 7.

The REME lessons of the campaign were digested and some changes in organisation were made before the landings in Sicily. The technical lessons led to the setting up of an experimental unit based in a workshop. Various projects were undertaken in North Africa, notably the up-gunning of Churchills using 75mm guns and mantlets from wrecked Shermans. Another less well-known exploit was the installation in a Mark I ARV of a winch. This was driven by the tank's main engine using a clutch and a worm-drive to take the power through a 90° angle, to rotate the vertical shaft of the winch which was mounted above the turret ring. A bollard at each corner of the hull allowed the winch rope to be used at any angle. This experimental ARV suffered from the frequent failure of winch-drive components, as they were not robust enough to transmit the engine's power.

# Chapter 5
# 1942–1944 Further Developments in the United Kingdom

The Home Forces in the United Kingdom were greatly reinforced from the beginning of 1942 by American troops including a growing airforce contingent. The country was described at this time as being 'one big training camp'. By providing camps, training areas, airfields, administrative services and some domestic transport for the US forces, Britain was able to discharge its obligation to the two-way concept of Lend-Lease. From mid-1942 planning had centred on Operation TORCH, the invasion of North Africa. With the successful accomplishment of this campaign the main emphasis shifted to an eventual landing in France.

The efficiency of the systems in Britain for developing and providing military equipment was slowly being improved with growing cooperation between the War Office and MOS and a greater awareness of the practical needs of the armies in the field. The initial testing of prototypes and imported equipment was carried out in the MOS trials establishments followed by War Office troop trials before acceptance for production. Often this more protracted

procedure had to be telescoped to hasten the start of production. When the War Office was persuaded that a stock US vehicle could meet its needs, development time was saved and vehicles were obtained through Lend-Lease. Progressive development and improvement of British tanks was pursued both by the War Office and MOS. The Crusader tank led to a new series, Cavalier, Centaur and later Cromwell, all similar in appearance. Only the latter two were to see operational service and the Cromwell was the first to use the new Meteor V12 engine, an adaptation of the Rolls Royce Merlin used in aircraft. Armament progressed through the 6-pounder to a dual purpose 75mm gun which could use the same ammunition as the US guns in the Grant and Sherman. The Churchill tank had by this time become a much more reliable vehicle and, after a blooding in the Dieppe raid and an unspectacular appearance at El Alamein it first saw major action in Tunisia. Many specialised vehicles were also developed including amphibians, airportable light tanks and a variety of armoured vehicles tailormade for major assaults by land or sea against heavily defended positions.

The War Office Tank Repair and Recovery Committee, originally set up in 1940, had lapsed after the Dunkirk evacuation. It was revived in April 1941 under the new Director of Mechanical Maintenance, later to become Director of Mechanical Engineering (DME). Its tasks included the investigation of recovery techniques and equipment. To assess such equipment an Experimental Recovery Section was set up at Arborfield near Reading in October 1941 next to the Recovery and AFV Repair Training Centre RAOC. At first the Section was concerned mainly with trials of new recovery tractors and transporters and the design of improvements. Later, completely new vehicles were designed and prototypes built. By October 1942, when the ERS was transferred to REME, it consisted of two officers and twenty soldiers. It was to grow by the end of the war to a strength of 182. Later an Experimental Beach Recovery Section (EBRS) was formed and the two units worked in unison producing, among other things, spade anchors for Scammells and other recovery vehicles, a stowage bracket for the Scammell spare wheel and paying on gear for winches. An early ERS invention, destined to become standard equipment, was the Hollebone drawbar. This hinged, tubular, rigid tow bar enabled tracked vehicles to be towed more efficiently. It was necessary to make

*A spade anchor designed for the Scammell Pioneer breakdown tractor by the Experimental Beach Recovery Section.*

separate versions for British and US tanks to fit their different standard towing shackles. The name derived from Colonel J.E. Hollebone, who had been Commandant of the Recovery and AFV Repair Training Centre. Sadly, some of the equipment designed by the ERS could not be produced in sufficient quantity for widespread issue before the war ended. This was due to the lack of engineering capacity in Britain and the lower priority given to non-fighting equipment by the War Office and MOS.

Among the vehicle developments was a light recovery vehicle based on the chassis of the Bedford QL 4×4 tractor for the Bofors light anti-aircraft gun. In 1944, a new medium recovery tractor was designed, intended to become a standard vehicle for the likely protracted war against Japan. After tests of the US FWD 4×4 and Diamond T 6×6 chassis the new medium recovery vehicle was based on the chassis of the Mack NM 6×6 gun tractor which was already used by the British Army. The double rear wheels were accepted as it was cheaper and easier to obtain a standard vehicle. The recovery gear was based on the twin-boom design with booms similar to the Gar Wood type used on the Canadian version of the Mack LMSW. The vehicle was fitted with a 7-ton main winch, powered jib winches and was designed from the start with winch-rope paying on gear. All winch controls could be operated from the cab. Twin detachable spades were fitted, looking rather like gun trail legs. The vehicle was accepted for production but before more than a handful could be completed the war ended and contracts were cancelled.

In 1943 a new chassis was introduced for the standard gantry body. The Austin K6 was a normal control vehicle

*An incomplete prototype of the Mack recovery tractor designed by the Experimental Recovery Section REME.*

more widely used till then by the RAF. It used the same engine as the smaller 4-wheeled Austins and was therefore underpowered for the recovery role. It remained in Army service into the 1960s. By this time, the 3-ton gantry lorry, originally rated as a heavy breakdown vehicle, was regarded as a medium vehicle but, due to shortages of heavier machines, it was often issued to units in lieu of their proper entitlement.

While ERS worked on recovery trials new transporters were also tested at MOS establishments. At WVEE a modified Federal 604, the tractor for the 20-ton transporter, was fitted with a ballast body over the fifth wheel coupling and was used to tow a 40-ton transporter trailer, itself modified for the carriage of lengths of railway line. Liaison was close between ERS, WVEE and FVPE, the civilian manufacturers and representatives of allied armies. Other corps than REME had vested interests in this experimental work. ARVs were of concern to the RAC and tank transporters to the RASC. When US and Canadian vehicles were being tested their military personnel were to be found at ERS giving it a very cosmopolitan air.

An Airborne Forces Development Centre was set up at Amesbury in 1943 and among its many experiments was the air movement of vehicles. Much parallel work was going on in India, where air supply had been perfected to a high degree by the USAAF and RAF supplying units in Burma and airlifting war material to China. The only available aircraft was the C47, a cargo version of the Douglas Dakota, with a double door at the left side of the fuselage. The width of this doorway placed a limit on what types of equipment could be carried and long items had to be very narrow so they could be inserted into the doorway at an acute angle. The only way to carry vehicles much bigger than Jeeps was to dismantle them for reassembly on arrival. Most 3-tonners modified for air transport amounted to three aircraft loads but, in the absence of more suitable planes, this drill was adopted. The smallest available recovery vehicle worth considering was the Morris Commercial CDSW and an airportable version was designed. The complete chassis with rear axle detached could be fitted in one aircraft, while a second carried the vehicle body, recovery and welding gear and the crew. These projects were optimistically based on the safe arrival of all aircraft and this was likely only where total air superiority had been established. The later availability of the Hamilcar glider enabled some quite sizeable vehicles to be carried intact.

# Chapter 6
# The Campaigns in Sicily and Italy

There was an inevitable pause after the defeat of the Axis forces in Tunisia while the allied armies prepared to land in Sicily, Operation HUSKY. REME had to supervise the waterproofing of thousands of vehicles using kits and materials produced in the Middle East base workshops. There was also a colossal overhaul task to prepare the battle-worn vehicles of the two British armies for yet another campaign.

Combined airborne and seaborne landings of British, Canadian and US troops brought the war to the Italian homeland in July 1943. The British landings over the beaches were supported by REME 'beach bricks', including recovery detachments whose normal D8 tractors and Scammells were waterproofed to exacting standards, since so much depended on them and on the two Churchill ARVs which were also used. The beach bricks were designed to recover and repair vehicles and equipment during the landings before any workshops arrived.

The brief campaign on the island ended with the surrender of all Italian forces and the escape of some German troops across the Straits of Messina to mainland Italy. REME recovery units in Sicily gained a foretaste of what Italy was to offer; narrow roads in steep hilly areas where a single breakdown could cause serious delays in the advance of fighting formations and in the movement of supply columns. Further recommendations were made for the conversion of Diamond T tractors to enable them to be used in a dual role.

Two main landings placed allied troops ashore in Italy. A joint British/American landing at Salerno was accompanied by a direct crossing of the Straits of Messina by the 8th Army. Thinly spread German forces resisted strongly but then withdrew. A negotiated surrender of all Italian forces took place at this time but the Germans reinforced the country and, being in possession of most of it, were able to drag out the war by a series of fighting withdrawals to a succession of defended lines. At that time there were few first-class roads in Italy and the main German defences were in the mountains where communications were at their worst. The US 5th Army, including a large number of British troops, operated on the Western side of the country while the British 8th Army covered the Eastern side.

The German surrender came only a few days before the war ended in Northern Europe. The final year's battles were bedevilled not only by terrain and weather but by the constant withdrawals of men and equipment, first for the invasion of France in 1944 and then for Operation GOLDFLAKE in early 1945, a direct transfer via Southern France of reinforcements for 21st Army Group in Belgium and Holland.

In Italy logistic problems arose from the terrain, the climate, a vehicle fleet much of which had been worn out in Africa, difficult lateral communications over the mountains and for some time the absence of base repair facilities. This resulted in dependence on the distant workshops in North Africa and Egypt. Enemy action seemed to take a greater toll of equipment in the more confined space in which it could operate compared to the desert. Without nearby base workshops a heavy manufacturing and modification work-load fell on the mobile workshops, which coped only because when their parent formations were rested the workshops carried on.

Some new vehicles were shipped from Britain but most came from the USA and Canada. Reconditioned vehicles came from Egypt and North Africa as the workshops there gradually repaired the huge accumulation of war-damaged vehicles from the earlier campaigns. New vehicles were mostly shipped crated and had to be assembled on arrival. Another delaying factor was the destruction of the ports by the retreating Germans. Larger cargo vessels had to await the restoration of the docks at Naples and Bari. Throughout the campaign there was a shortage of fit vehicles and so the recovery and rapid repair of casualties was vital.

British workshops and recovery companies were to become more familiar here with US and Canadian 'wreckers' as the emphasis on replacement vehicles from these countries increased. The standard issue US and Canadian types have been described. Despite the availability of some of these wreckers there remained a shortage of recovery vehicles and, as in North Africa, workshops were called upon to improvise. Among local conversions were a Diamond T 980 tractor fitted with a complete Scammell breakdown body and a Mack NM 6×6 tractor similarly 'attired'. Another Mack NM was given the body from a CMP wrecker, its Gar Wood gear making it very similar to the vehicle under development at ERS. An unknown number of Mack NM and Diamond T 968 gun tractors were fitted with jibs of local design, one being the work of a REME welder named Crellin from 670 Army Recovery Company. So great was the need for these additional

*Diamond T 980 tank transporter tractor in Italy sporting a Scammell recovery body.*

*An improvisation from Italy. A Mack NM gun tractor fitted with a complete Scammell recovery body.*

*A Mack NM photographed in Trieste in about 1950. This was one of the conversions made in Canal Zone base workshops during 1943/44 for use in Italy.*

recovery vehicles that some were batch converted in the Canal Zone base workshops for the units in Italy. In some instances the original US gun tractor body was kept but with part of the floor removed where the jib was welded to the chassis. On another more elaborate version the original body was replaced by a redundant CMP 15-cwt or 30-cwt steel body mounted forward on the chassis which was exposed at the rear where the jib was fitted. Some of these local conversions remained in use into the 1950s in the Middle East and Austria.

In the appalling winter conditions on the undeveloped Italian mountain roads only Jeeps could operate and soon improvised recovery equipment was fitted to some of them. A small number of Morris Commercial CDSW light recovery tractors was still in service in 1943 and proved useful in the narrow mountain roads. The slow and costly assaults against defended lines in Italy contrasted strongly with the dashing movement in the desert and tanks were used far more in an infantry-support role in Italy. Transporters were used far more for recovery and backloading and less for the movement of fit tanks to save track wear. Improvisation was not confined to recovery tractors. In Italy some 20-ton semi-trailers from the ill-starred Albion CX24 were fitted to Federal or similar Reo 6×4 tractors. Little is recorded of their employment. At some time after the war some of these semi-trailers were to appear in French Army use fitted to tractors using the Diamond T 4-ton 6×6 chassis. Some Albions did continue in their original role but at a reduced load capacity. As in North Africa captured German recovery equipment was utilised including the

*A Diamond T 968 artillery tractor converted to recovery vehicle during the Italian campaign.*

*A jeep recovery vehicle used in an infantry brigade workshop.*

*The US M31 Tank Recovery vehicle based on the M3, General Lee, tank, shown here in Italy recovering a derelict Sherman.*

complex Sd Ah 116 23-ton transporter trailer which was fitted with a detachable 4 wheeled bogie at the rear and bore a superficial resemblance to the 1928 RAOC Aldershot design.

Early in the Italian campaign the US Army introduced its T2 (later M31) ARV which is described in Chapter 7. Two Churchill ARVs Mark I were sent to Italy from North Africa for a comparative trial against the T2 and showed up rather poorly. A Mechanical Warfare Experimental Establishment had been set up at Ottaviana near Naples and one of its tasks was the development of a winch-equipped ARV. This too used a Churchill hull and a winch from a Diamond T tractor driven by a Morris Commercial engine. Preliminary trials were satisfactory but there is no record of any subsequent conversions. In the meantime six of the US T2s were issued to REME and were widely used. Later the Sherman based M32 ARV was also taken into use by the British Army. Some Grant tank tugs were also issued for recovery in Italy. There, as elsewhere, unarmoured tracked tractors were widely used.

In the USA before the war some experimental tracked amphibians had been used in the Florida swamplands. Later, military versions called Landing Vehicles Tracked (LVTs) were to form the vanguard of the many US Marine landings in the Pacific. The final wartime variant, LVT4, was a cargo carrier with a sealed rear ramp and, in some instances, light armour. It could carry small vehicles or up to four tons of cargo. A small number of LVT4s were issued to British forces towards the end of the operations in Italy for an attack in the area of Lake Commachio. Somewhat typically the British Army decided to produce several modified versions shortly before the operation began. The work was mostly carried out in great haste by 686 Infantry Troops Workshop and included a recovery variant. The code name for all LVTs in Italy was Fantail whereas in North West Europe LVT4s used by 79th Armoured Division were called Buffaloes.

The Recovery Fantail was created by the fairly simple

*The LVT 4 in Italy fitted out as an ARV using a gun tractor chassis with winch inside the cargo well.*

expedient of fitting into the cargo well the truncated and wheel-less chassis of a gun tractor, complete with its engine and bonnet. A roller was set up on a frame extended vertically so that the winch cable could operate clear of the raised rear ramp of the LVT. Drive to the winch was via the tractor's normal gearbox power take-off. A few of these conversions were made to provide amphibious recovery support to operational LVTs. The official REME war history states that Morris gun tractors were used but photos show a CMP type. It is most likely that other unrecorded recovery vehicle conversions took place in Italy but those described here give a good example of the ingenuity of REME tradesmen when left to make their own tools.

Another interesting aside was the revelation by a German POW that two Sherman tanks captured in the Anzio bridgehead were taken to Rome and modified into turretless ARVs and successfully used by the Germans in this role.

# Chapter 7
# 1942–1945 Armoured Recovery Vehicles and New Transporters

After the salvage tanks of World War I and various half-hearted proposals for such machines between the wars nothing much happened until RAOC and REME experience led to experiments mainly at Arborfield beginning in February 1942. The War Office was convinced of the need for a protected recovery vehicle but it was not till 1942 that a sufficient output of tanks from Britain, Canada and the USA made it possible to divert some earlier tanks for experiments in non-fighting roles. Initially, tests were made using turretless tanks as towing vehicles but increasing their rated drawbar pull by the use of a pulley and cable layout with ground anchors when extracting another tank from a difficult position. Trials of a Churchill and a Covenanter tank in the ARV role began in April 1942. The Covenanter was quickly discarded as unsuitable and work continued with the Churchill. The design that became ARV Mark I used a turretless tank with the hull fighting compartment roofed over. A hatchway gave access for the recovery crew. Somewhat later an AA machine-gun mounting, designed in the ERS, was fitted internally and could be raised to fire the guns through the hatch in the roof without exposing the gunner. Additional stowage bins and racks festooned the vehicles, and equipment carried included hand tools, short and long cables, Hollebone drawbars, several snatchblocks, a good supply of ground anchor plates and 'pins' (an inappropriate name for a three foot steel bar weighing several pounds). A dismountable tubular steel derrick was carried which could be erected at the front of the ARV and used with a block and tackle or portable winch to lift major tank components.

By October 1942 Crusader and Grant ARVs were being tested. The Crusader too was discarded but a few Grants were converted and used mainly for training. The Grant as well as being turretless had the main gun removed from its side sponson. Recovery crews had to learn how to split tracks so as to remove them from damaged tanks if necessary. To avoid wear and tear some track pins on the ARVs used for this training were adapted for easy removal and the appropriate track links painted white.

It became obvious that for standardisation it would be necessary to make an ARV variant of each main type of gun tank so that the ARV was compatible for major spare parts supply. Cavalier, Centaur and Cromwell ARVs soon followed and both Sherman and Ram variants. All except the Ram followed the usual design but with the Canadian tank, developed at Arborfield with the Royal Canadian Ordnance Corps (RCOC), the turret was retained and a manually operated winch was fitted. When the Comet tank came into service in 1945 its weight was little more than that of the Cromwell and the need for yet another ARV was avoided. Production of the Churchill ARV Mark I commenced in mid-1942 and the first dozen were used in the North Africa campaign. The need for a winch was realised but no source of supply could then be found as all British and US manufacturers were fully committed, mainly on naval contracts. After the first use of ARVs in Tunisia the winch requirement became a high priority. The ARVs Mark I would have been less effective as recovery vehicles than the

*The Grant ARV Mark I towing a Diamond T 980 tank transporter with British 40-ton trailer and Churchill tank.*

*Cromwell ARV Mark I.*

*Demonstration of Ram ARV Mark I at Arborfield during 1942.*

*Sherman ARV Mark I during North West Europe campaign. The tracks are fitted with grousers, extension pieces, to reduce the vehicle's ground pressure on soft terrain.*

D8 tractor were it not for their better speed and protection.

In 1943 the ERS began to develop a winch-equipped ARV Mark II which would be built on three tanks only, Churchill, Sherman and Ram, the latter intended for Canadian use but built to a common design. The Mark II featured a fixed structure over the turret space fitted with a dummy gun to disguise its specialist role. This structure housed the winch, obtained from Crofts of Bradford, and the crew members less the driver who sat in the hull. The winch of the Churchill version was driven by the vehicle's engine and could exert a 25-ton direct pull. The cable paid out to the rear through an aperture in the back of the superstructure and passed over a pulley on a small fixed jib at the rear of the tank. This jib provided a heavy lift whereas the detachable booms at the front, as fitted to the Mark I, were retained for lighter lifts for assembly changes. A hinged spade was fitted at the rear of the hull and could be lowered, then driven into the ground by reversing the vehicle, which was not then solely dependent on its own weight as an anchor when winching. A selection of recovery equipment was carried as on the Mark I. At Hazely Heath, some miles from Arborfield, a winch test rig was built comprising a ramp with a short length of railway line. The winches were tested drawing a ballasted rail wagon up the ramp. ERS built some pilot Mark II ARVs, including four of the Churchills. MOS was glad to be freed from these experiments so as to concentrate on gun tank development but when the new ARVs were ready for production MOS arranged contracts. Due to a shortage of engineering capacity many of the conversions took place in REME workshops. Five hundred Mark II ARVs were ordered but very few had been completed when the war ended and commercial contracts were cancelled. For some years after the war many units had to make do with Mark I ARVs or with none at all so some conversions of Churchills continued for a few years at 13 Command Workshop at Aldershot.

Parallel ARV development took place in the USA where they were known as 'Tank Retrievers' or 'Tank Recovery Vehicles'. The first US ARV to see service was the T2 (M31) based on the M3 tank (General Lee). This was designed from the start with a winch. The smaller M3 turret was turned to the rear and, in place of the gun, a crane jib was fitted. A dummy gun was sometimes welded to what had been the turret rear. The turret could still rotate so the crane could be slewed to any angle. Stays at the side of the jib could be attached to the tank hull to support heavy lifts to the rear or extended to ground level to support lifts to the side. The main fighting compartment of the tank housed the

*The Sherman ARV Mark II illustrating the 'Christmas tree' appearance of such vehicles.*

*Churchill ARV Mark II with the front lifting booms erected.*

*The M32, known in British Service as Sherman ARV Mark III.*

winch. In British service the M31 was known as the Grant ARV Mark II. One major drawback of the vehicle was the absence of a spade anchor. Some M31s had a dummy main gun on the sponson on the right side of the hull. Although used operationally the M31 was only an interim design.

The M32 was a more effective vehicle based on an M4 (Sherman) hull. Like the British Mark II ARV this had a fixed structure in place of the turret, the sides of which were angled, giving a coffin shape in plan view. This was to accommodate the two booms of a fixed A frame hinged to the top of the hull at the front and lowered to the rear for travelling. The A frame provided a heavy lift for major assemblies and could be used for engine or even turret changes. The vehicle was fitted with a 30(US)-ton main winch and the winch cable could be run out to the front of the vehicle for recovery or lifting and to the rear for lifting. No fixed spade was fitted but small detachable chocks were carried which were placed under the tracks as a form of anchor. A number of sub-variants of this vehicle existed depending on the basic type of Sherman used for the conversion. A main armament was provided in the shape of an externally mounted 81mm mortar. These were usually discarded. Some of the M32s were issued to British units in Italy and continued in use for some years after the war, particularly in the Middle East, and they were designated Sherman ARV Mark III.

The US range of medium tanks was to have been complemented by a heavy tank weighing about 50 tons and designated M6. Its design found little favour with the US Army which was frequently at odds with the US Ordnance Department, the design and procurement agency, over projected equipment, echoing the British situation between the War Office and MOS. The tank, had it gone into quantity production, was earmarked for British use through Lend-Lease. Other very heavy British armoured vehicles were projected and some, like the 70-ton Tortoise tank destroyer, were eventually built. With these prospects in mind a heavy trailer was called for and, once again, Cranes produced a remarkable design.

The prototype 70-ton trailer was built in 1943 and consisted of a two-part frame, hinged so as to cross undulations in the ground. The front half carried two rows of four wheels and the rear half, three rows of four wheels. Ackerman steering operated on the four outer rows of wheels. The tank-carrying bed was attached to the frame in such a way that it could be tilted, bringing the rear close to the ground so that, using two small hinged ramps, tanks could be driven or winched on board. As a tank reached the point of balance it depressed the front of the bed into its horizontal travelling mode. The tilting of an empty trailer was achieved by a single hydraulic ram operated by a hand-pump. A small production batch of these trailers was built by Elliot and Garood and they were used from 1944 to carry various experimental and captured German tanks and, eventually, for the Tortoise. Some 70-ton trailers continued in use well into the 1950s. Yet another product of Cranes was a 20-ton capacity platform trailer to carry the D8 tractor. It had 16 wheels in two rows of eight, the front row being turntable steered. The suspension system was similar to that of the 24-wheeled 40-ton trailer.

The shortage of off-road recovery transporters, due to the slow production of Scammells, led to a proposal to convert the more readily available Diamond T tractor to take a semi-trailer. Trials began in December 1942 at WVEE and later at ERS of a tractor with a fifth wheel coupling replacing the ballast body and a Scammell 30-ton semi-trailer. The trials were successful and, since Scammells could not increase semi-trailer production, a new 30-ton semi-trailer was designed and built by Shelvoke and Drewry. The production package included the fifth wheel coupling and mountings so that conversion was a relatively simple task. Two hundred trailers were produced and

*The Cranes 70-ton tilt bed transporter trailer lightly loaded with a prototype A20 tank hull.*

*The Diamond T articulated transporter with Shelvoke and Drewry semi-trailer.*

conversion of the tractors was undertaken by MOS. When some Scammell tractors later became available, due to a surplus of 20-ton transporters, some were fitted with the Shelvoke and Drewry semi-trailers.

Many tank transporters were used for the carriage of other heavy equipment but one novel use for a Rogers 40-ton trailer was as the basis for an experimental 90-barrelled rocket launcher built in 1945 at the School of Artillery.

In 1942 the US Fruehauf Trailer Company designed a new front-line articulated tank transporter. The original tractor design was sub-contracted to the Knuckey Truck Company but this small concern handed over production to the larger Pacific Car and Foundry Company. The vehicle consisted of an armoured 6×6 tractor unit, given the company's model number TR-1 and US Army designation M26 together with a 40(US)-ton semi-trailer M15. The combination was officially Truck Trailer Transporter M25 but unofficially the Dragon Wagon. The semi-trailer could be detached and the tractor driven away to recover a tank using its two main winches with a combined pull of 60(US)-tons. A detachable jib structure enabled the tractor to be used for suspended tows of B Vehicles. Later versions of the semi-trailer were uprated to 45 tons and long after the war were used with newer tractors carrying well over 50-ton loads.

Later versions of the Pacific tractor, designated M26A1, were unarmoured. Both types were powered by massive Hall Scott six-cylinder petrol engines. In all over 1,300 were built. An unknown quantity was allocated to the British Army and one was modified at the FVPE as a ballast tractor and was fitted with single wheels with 21.00×24 tyres. Another standard M25 was photographed just after the war with a British Army number. Some ex-WD Pacifics had an extended life as heavy haulage tractors in the Robert Wynns fleet.

Towards the end of the war a new Heavy Cruiser tank was developed. This was the A41 which was later named Centurion. The first production versions reached the troops in Germany just too late to be tested in action. The tank was powered by the Meteor engine previously used in the Cromwell and Comet. Centurion weighed nearly 50 tons, creating a need for a heavier transporter. Cranes produced a prototype by the end of 1945 which was essentially a widened and lengthened 40-tonner with the turntable fitted with two lines of stub axles instead of a single line. There were, therefore, 32 wheels instead of 24. A very similar trailer was to be produced by R.A. Dyson after the war.

Feedback from the campaign in North Africa provided much of the impetus for early experiments at ERS. The problems of tank recovery in soft and uneven ground and the limitations of existing recovery vehicles and transporters led to much effort in the development of off-road transporters. An early Cranes design has been described. A later Cranes design for a 45-ton trailer was a great deal simpler in concept and, through the use of massive 16.00×20 earth moving equipment tyres, it was a useful off-road trailer. It

*Cranes 45-ton tank transporter trailer towed by a modified Diamond T model 980 fitted with single rear wheels.*

*An early tracked trailer with built-in winch being tested with a Churchill hulk as a load. This may be the original NLE equipment carrier.*

*The Cranes designed but Boulton and Paul built tracked tank recovery trailer.*

had a built-in engine-powered winch but was extremely high due to the large tyres and as a result was probably unstable when loaded. Tests had also been carried out of tracked transporter trailers. The earliest had originally been designed for an entirely different enterprise called 'Nellie'. In France in 1939 much thought had been given to how troops would cross the fire-swept ground in front of the German Siegfried Line. Mr Churchill, once again at the Admiralty, with echoes of the earlier war, used Royal Navy resources to develop a huge trench-digging machine which, it was envisaged, would carve a trench six or more feet deep, enabling assault troops to approach the line safe from machine-gun fire. Nellie was an acronym based on the letters NLE, Naval Land Equipment, and one machine was built and successfully tested. The fall of France saved it from operational use where its purpose might well have been thwarted by plunging mortar and howitzer fire. The trailers made to carry components of Nellie ran on small tracked bogies and were ideal for testing the theory of off-road tank transporters.

An improved trailer was designed by Cranes, and later mass-produced by Boulton and Paul, an aircraft manufacturer. This was fitted with tracked bogies made by the firm Roadless Traction, the front ones on a steering turntable. On production versions of the trailer a housing at the front concealed an engine-driven winch to enable the trailer to load tanks independent of the tractor. By the time this development had progressed the ARV was in existence and was the obvious towing vehicle. The trailer was officially rated at 45-tons load but could carry much more. It was itself so heavy and unsuitable for use on roads that it had to be carried on a wheeled transporter. This and the prospect of better off-road wheeled transporters meant that the tracked trailer was little used. One at least carried diesel railway locomotives to France and was able to traverse the beaches from a landing craft with its heavy burden.

Drawings held in the Tank Museum and originating from the School of Tank Technology show a number of other off-road tank transporter designs which are not known to have progressed beyond the stage of these concept sketches. Some of these ideas were also recorded in an early post-war monograph on REME history. One scheme was for a tilt bed trailer resting on two centrally mounted tracked bogies but with a pair of solid tyred stabiliser wheels at each end. The vehicle would have been towed by another tank. Presumably the rear stabiliser wheels would fold away to enable the trailer bed to tilt for loading. A second scheme proposed a similar rig without stabilisers but fitted with a massive swan neck which was attached to a fifth wheel coupling in the centre of the turret ring of a turretless Churchill. An hydraulic ram above the fifth wheel would raise the swan neck, thus tilting the trailer whose main frame was pivoted on the transverse centre line of the tracked bogie. Two stabilising hydraulic rams connected the trailer frame to the rear of the tank hull. The third scheme was for a three-quarter tracked 40-ton transporter with folding rear ramps. The forward control truck cab was to be armoured and a steerable front axle would have been based on a Diamond T rear axle. The main transporter frame would have rested on the tracks and suspension of the 50-ton US M6 tank. The proposed engine was the Bedford twin six of the Churchill tank. One design shown in the sketches did reach the prototype stage. A Scammell 30-ton semi-trailer with Roadless Traction tracked bogies in place of its rear wheels was tested in the continued quest for an off-road transporter. The tractor was a Diamond T with single tyred rear wheels and overall tracks.

The common solution to inadequate engine-power in vehicles had long been to install two engines. There were numerous examples of this in World War II and one directly concerning this subject was a heavy tractor developed by Albion Motors. This was designed as a safeguard against interruptions in the supply of Diamond T tractors. In fact this did not happen so only the prototype CX33 appeared. It used four close-coupled axles all driven by the two Albion engines but in later experiments drive to one axle was disconnected giving it an 8×6 drive line. The vehicle could tow a 75-ton load and was fitted with a winch, the controls for which were in a cabin at the rear, giving the vehicle a double-ended appearance. Another experimental vehicle tested as a tank tractor was a 6-wheel drive version of the Scammell Pioneer gun tractor.

Vehicle waterproofing experiments had begun well before World War II with river crossing and amphibious landings in mind. With the setting up of a Combined Operations Staff after Dunkirk these experiments were intensified and

*Modified Scammell 30-ton semi-trailer with tracked bogies. The tractor is a Diamond T with single wheels and overall tracks. A Matilda Infantry Tank Mark II is the load.*

*The experimental Scammell Pioneer 6×6 gun tractor towing a Crusader tank in tests at Arborfield.*

were tested in action in Madagascar and later in the various landings in the Mediterranean. The big test came on D Day, 6 June 1944. A landing over enemy held beaches posed many recovery problems and it was decided that special ARVs would be needed. Experiments with operational techniques and specialised equipment were conducted by the joint Navy/Army Combined Operations Experimental Establishment (COXE). Wadeproofing trials units existed at Instow and Weymouth and many trials were carried out in Scotland.

In 1943 EBRS was established at Appledore and formed REME's link with COXE. EBRS later moved to Budleigh Salterton, where among trials carried out were those of the wadeproofed D8 tractor, later named the Porpoise, and the Sherman Beach Armoured Recovery Vehicle (BARV). Both were designed to wade in deep water and to pull 'drowned' vehicles out of the sea. The concept for the BARV led, in October 1943, to attempts to modify the early Churchill and Sherman ARVs Mark I by simply fitting a box over the turret ring to give clearance above wave level. The problems of sealing the Churchill hull soon led to concentration on the Sherman. Work on the early version, the Ford-engined M4A3 (British Sherman Mark IV) was not wasted as the square box structure over the turret space became the standard deep-wading fitment for the normal Mark I ARVs required to land over the beaches in Normandy.

The design of the definitive BARV commenced at ERS Arborfield and was based on the Sherman Mark III (M4A2) with twin GMC diesel engines, chosen partly because these tanks were more readily available from Lend-Lease allocations. It featured a welded, boat-shaped armoured superstructure above the level of the hull. A hatchway directly above the turret ring was the only way in and out. The driver's and co-driver's positions, which when wading lay below water level, were sealed and fitted with small armoured-glass vision blocks. For all practical purposes driving the tank depended on the vehicle commander's view from above. Trials, which began on 22 December 1943, soon showed the need for modification. Production vehicles were given a splash lip around the top of the superstructure and fitted with a 'nosing' plate, a form of buffer at the front, which was padded with rope and used for pushing armoured vehicles or beached landing craft. The special equipment within the vehicle included a bilge pump. In its final form the Sherman BARV could operate in water depths of 9 feet with an 18 inch surge. The ideal of a built-in winch was sacrificed to help speed up production. 21st Army Group bid for 50 BARVs and then asked for more. MOS organised production and by D-Day 52 vehicles were available; achieved only by the loan of 80 REME tradesmen to the firms building them. Before D-Day the first production vehicles had been used at the wading and waterproofing trials establishments where their attributes were invaluable. BARV crews had to be able to connect

*Trials of an early Sherman BARV.*

*The final version of the BARV giving joy rides to some of the DME's staff on the day victory in Europe was declared.*

tow-cables to vehicles under water, so a special shallow-water diving rig was developed for their use. It was a somewhat bulky ancestor of the present-day scuba diving gear. Diving training was given by the Navy. The Sherman BARV remained in service long after the war ended.

The Caterpillar D8 tractor with its very low ground pressure was ideal for work on beaches and its use in trials at the EBRS soon led to its selection as an alternative to the BARV. The wadeproofed tractor was fitted with an armoured body and its winch gave it one advantage over the BARV for recovery work. Armoured bodies for the D8 were built at 5 Command Workshop REME at Buntingford. Some of these tractors also remained in service long after the war with the Army and Royal Marines. REME occasionally used other armoured tractors based on the Caterpillar D7 and International TD 18 tractors, but these were not primarily intended either for recovery or beach work. Most were used as bulldozers by the RE. These vehicles had waterproofed engines but the armoured cabs were not sealed for deep wading.

# Chapter 8
# D Day and the North West Europe Campaign

Even before the USA entered the war Britain had begun to plan a return to the European mainland. From 1942 the British Combined Operations Staffs expanded into a special planning organisation for what was to become Operation OVERLORD, a major landing from the sea of British, US and Canadian forces in Normandy. The overall commander was General Eisenhower but the land forces commander for the invasion was General Montgomery. Planning and preparation gathered momentum in early 1944 and, after a 24-hour postponement, troops were landed on the 6 June. The British element, 21st Army Group, was to become known as the British Liberation Army (BLA).

The years of planning for REME had involved mainly the techniques of waterproofing vehicles and the preparation of equipment and trained units for beach recovery. The REME tradesmen attached to the 27th Armoured Brigade (amphibious Duplex Drive (DD) tanks) were early on the beaches but the first of all REME units ashore on D Day were the beach recovery sections equipped with Sherman BARVs, the waterproofed D8 tractors and some un-armoured Scammells. Their crews carried out much of the initial recovery work, often under fire and over ground containing mines. There were inevitably some REME casualties. The vital task was to clear beaches of damaged or 'drowned' vehicles so they would not impede the follow-up vehicles nor foul landing craft coming in on a higher tide. The prepared exits from beaches, often narrow gaps in sea

walls, had to be kept open at all costs. Drowned vehicles which had suffered waterproofing failures amounted to only a few per cent. More usually they were vehicles which had been landed in water too deep. All were collected together in special parks, where they could be dried out and refurbished by follow-up workshops. Parks for damaged vehicles were also set up, all part of the hectic activity of the beach recovery organisation. Another task was the towing away of beach defences, steel girders used as barriers to landing craft and vehicles.

Both the BARVs and D8s worked well. Reports from the sections suggested some improvements including the fitting of a winch to the BARV. The D8 was very slow and it was difficult to communicate with the driver from outside over the noise of the engine and the surrounding battle. It was proposed that an external telephone should be fitted as on tanks.

Even on this grim day there was some light relief. The driver of a D8 was injured in the hand by fragments of bullets which entered his cab through vision slits. Ordered to report to a first-aid post he stopped to ask a Royal Navy beachmaster the way. This august warrior was directing operations accompanied by his dog. The injured REME driver was detailed to take the dog for a walk on his way to the first-aid post! BARVs were later used during the Rhine crossing and D8s during the landings in the Scheldt estuary. The beach recovery sections were reorganised later as

*Four wade-proofed D8 tractors dislodge a tank which had sunk into a quicksand on the Normandy beach.*

normal recovery sections and re-equipped.

The success of the Normandy landings was due in no small measure to the specialised vehicles designed by Britain to support the armies in the difficult period between being afloat and being established inland from the beaches. The campaign following the breakout from the Normandy bridgehead and, after the Falaise battle, involved a swift pursuit of German forces into Belgium followed by the thrust for the Rhine bridges, with Operation MARKET GARDEN culminating in the disaster of Arnhem. Operations then concentrated on clearing the Scheldt estuary of Germans so that shipping could deliver supplies direct to Antwerp and ease the congested supply lines still stretching back to Normandy. Following the defeat of Hitler's surprise offensive in the Ardennes in December 1944 the battles swept into Germany up to the Rhine. The river was crossed in a mini-Normandy invasion using amphibious vehicles, landing craft and supported by another massive airborne landing. The British forces drove on into North Germany while the Canadian Army liberated Northern Holland and US and French forces entered Central and Southern Germany. Sandwiched between Russians moving westwards and the British and US Armies moving east the German nation capitulated in May 1945, ending the war in Europe.

The nature of the war in this theatre, varying from major assaults on well-fortified defensive positions to swift pursuit actions punctuated by short bloody engagements, gave the recovery units much dangerous and difficult work. LADs and workshops and REME tradesmen in other units remained responsible for most front-line recovery. The 13 REME recovery companies cleared battlefields and back-loaded damaged tanks to the base workshops which were set up by August 1944. With many formations moving on parallel routes all available roads, often small country lanes, had to be utilised regardless of their suitability for the movement of armoured vehicles. Attempts to pass broken-down vehicles often caused weak verges to collapse and vehicles to topple into ditches. Recovery had somehow to deal with the task without blocking the route still further.

Most of the types of recovery vehicle developed during the war years plus the Scammell and some gantry lorries of

*A Scammell Pioneer breakdown tractor of 176 Infantry Brigade Workshop in early 1945 in Germany.*

pre-war design were to be found among units of the 21st Army Group. No entirely new types of wheeled recovery vehicle were issued during this campaign but the gantry vehicles in use included a number of the newer Austins. A few of the improved version of the Ward La France (US designation Heavy Wrecker M1A1) were used by British Army units. These were fitted with canvas-topped cabs and. like the later Diamond T tank transporter tractors, they were rated as pneumonia wagons in the bitter 1944/45 winter. Many old lessons were re-learned in this campaign, one being the need to have cranes available in workshops to avoid tying up recovery vehicles in this subsidiary role.

*An Austin 3-ton 6×4 breakdown gantry lorry with a tracked ambulance and Bedford OY 3-tonner on tow photographed here in the 1950s.*

A small number of the Scammells and other heavy recovery vehicles had benefitted from the efforts of the ERS at Arborfield and were equipped with spade anchors; and various official and unofficial modifications of vehicles took place. Some Scammells were fitted with armour plate over the engine and one at least had the cycle-type front mudguards replaced by angled fixed mudguards. Some modification kits were issued for fitting pendulum paying-on gear for the winches of US vehicles in an effort to preserve cables. In 22 Advanced Base Workshop a very unusual Diamond T 980 was used. In its ballast body a large girder crane was fitted which had been taken from a commercial lorry in UK.

The need to move new and reconditioned tanks on trailers continued in this theatre and nine RASC tank transporter companies formed part of 21st Army Group's logistic support. The great pressure on roads led to schemes for carrying greater loads on fewer vehicles so a large number of 40-ton transporter trailers were adapted for load carrying. Huge quantities of ammunition, a particularly dense commodity, could be carried. To make the trailers more suitable for this role a number were fitted with detachable sides made of pierced steel planking, a material intended for runways on emergency airfields. After trials in the United Kingdom some transporters were used to carry Navy Landing Craft from the Channel ports to the River

*The final version of the US Heavy Wrecker, the M1A1 built by Ward La France and Kenworth. This was photographed early in 1945 in REME use.*

*A Diamond T tractor fitted with a commercial crane in its ballast body. The cylindrical device appearing at the end of the jib is a distant water tower.*

*A Mack LMSW breakdown tractor tows a modified Rogers 40-ton trailer used as a landing craft transporter.*

*A Dyson 40-ton transporter trailer being fitted with side panels for use as a cargo carrier. This trailer is being modified in 22 Advanced Base Workshop in Cormelles in France in 1944.*

*A German Stug III assault gun captured by 835 Heavy Recovery Section in Normandy and adapted as an ARV.*

Rhine to assist with the crossing. In some cases the craft were carried on a swivelling cradle and could be launched into a river or canal direct from the side of the trailer.

The shortage of ARVs meant that they were issued mainly to armoured regiments and armoured brigade workshops. It soon became clear that, as infantry brigade workshops were frequently called on to support armoured units and provide recovery support, these workshops should acquire ARVs. Short-term expedients were captured German tanks. A Panzer IV was used by one workshop with the gun removed and the aperture in the mantlet sealed with armoured glass. The vehicle was decked out with khaki paint, allied white star markings and recovery gear. Another workshop captured a pre-war French Hotchkiss tank which had been used by the Wehrmacht and adapted it as an ARV. Later in the campaign another Panzer IV was used and kept by the workshop until the Rhine crossing. In August 1944 835 Heavy Recovery Section acquired a German Stug III assault gun and this, minus gun, became a temporary ARV. A beach recovery section made use of two ex-French Army Somua MCL5 half tracks. Another recovery section made use of a captured 18 ton half track and Ah 116 trailer. There were probably many other unrecorded instances of the use of captured vehicles for recovery.

Workshops and units were, at this time, dependent on Mark I ARVs; Cromwells and Shermans in armoured divisions and Churchills, mostly in the Army tank brigades. Any recovery task requiring a winch still fell to the D8s, mainly unarmoured, and the wheeled tractors. Some REME officers and soldiers received decorations for carrying out recovery tasks under fire or in minefields and many casualties were suffered during such actions. The first Churchill Mark II ARVs reached units just before the Rhine crossing, a few months before the war ended in Europe. Their greater usefulness was welcomed.

As the North West Europe campaign progressed and the outcome became more certain much thought was given to the eventual withdrawal of units and their transfer to the Far East for the war against Japan. The US government began to seem disinclined to meet Lend-Lease demands for vehicles and equipment with such open-handedness as before and the massive reinforcements planned for Burma would therefore entail much refurbishment of existing equipment. There was an incentive therefore to recover and repair everything reusable not only with the requirements of the immediate campaign in mind. In the meantime there was some bitterness in the British camp at the seemingly lavish scale of equipment available to the US Army and the way in which it was so easily discarded. This probably reflected the facts that Britain had been at war longer than the USA, its homeland had been severely mauled and both military and civilian alike had endured for so long a level of austerity completely unknown to Americans.

For many soldiers release from the Army was not to come for a year or more after the war ended. The recovery companies in Europe had a huge task of battlefield clearance and many German armoured vehicles were required back in the UK for technical assessment. One journey, again by 835 Heavy Recovery Section, involved moving a Jagd Tiger, the heaviest German assault gun, on an adapted Reichsbahn (German railways) solid-tyred trailer which was towed by a Diamond T. This trip to Hamburg, where the vehicle was embarked, took several months including long waits while war-damaged bridges were strengthened or rebuilt. Before the war had even ended some Tigers and King Tigers were recovered from Normandy using the Cranes 70-ton trailers.

The end of the war in Europe was officially celebrated on the 8 May 1945 but amidst the euphoria many people struggled to remind the public that the war against Japan continued. Even those who knew about the atomic bomb could not predict its effect on Japan and there was no prospect then of an early end to the war.

# Chapter 9
# The War Against Japan: India and South East Asia

The Indian Army, since 1857, had been an independent force funded by the Indian Government. The officers and most technical personnel were British and the remainder were native-born Indians. Units of the British Army also served in India, mainly on the North West Frontier with Afghanistan. Although there were differences of organisation and equipment between the two armies these did not prevent easy integration, where necessary, of units from both armies into a joint force. It is because of this level of integration and the service of REME personnel with the Indian Electrical and Mechanical Engineers (IEME) that the equipment of the Indian Army is included in this book. Repairs to equipment were largely the responsibility of the Indian Army Ordnance Corps (IAOC) which had absorbed the entire repair organisation of the Royal Indian Army Service Corps (RIASC) in April 1939. In 1943 IEME was formed from the Workshop Branch of IAOC. The government of India, inevitably as it was part of the British Empire, rallied to the cause when war was declared in 1939 and Indian Army units were soon fighting alongside British.

Before Japan invaded British possessions in the Far East in 1941 the main deployment of Indian Army formations had been in the Middle East and East Africa. The additional manpower needed to meet the threat from Japan was achieved by a massive expansion of the Indian Army. The Japanese invasion of Malaya, Hong Kong and Burma resulted in yet more disaster and defeat for Britain. The hastily expanded Indian Army served and suffered in these countries and, in the Malaya campaign, Australian and British reinforcements arrived just in time to be captured in Singapore. Thereafter the main British action was in Assam and Northern Burma. British troops, including some veterans of the early part of the North African campaign, fought a rearguard action as they withdrew northwards through Burma to the hoped for security of India. The Burmese terrain includes some grassy plains, much hardwood forest but, further north, only jungle-covered mountains. Roads were few and when the allied survivors crossed the Chindwin river most vehicles were abandoned on the enemy side.

Reinforcements, including US forces, were rushed to northern India in order to protect supply routes to China through which the USA supplied the Chinese Nationalist forces in their long-standing war against the Japanese. Controlled from India, the Army element of South East

Asia Command (SEAC) was known as Allied Land Forces South East Asia (ALFSEA). Cooperating with the British Empire forces in north Burma were a number of Chinese divisions whose efforts were mainly coordinated by US troops.

By 1944, after abortive campaigns in 1942–43 in the Arakan peninsula, the bulk of the British and Indian formations were concentrated in Assam when the Japanese assaults fell on Kohima and Imphal. Here, for the first time, the enemy was soundly defeated and the allied armies went over to the offensive which continued southwards without pause until, by mid-1945, the Japanese Army had been virtually destroyed. Rangoon, the main Burmese port, was re-occupied and, following the use of atomic bombs, the war in the Far East ended in August enabling the planned invasion of Malaya, Operation ZIPPER, to take place unopposed. The brunt of the war against Japan was borne by US forces which fought their way from one Pacific island to the next reaching Okinawa not long before the war ended. Australian troops cleared the Japanese from New Guinea in jungle conditions every bit as dreadful as those in Burma.

As the Indian Army expanded and at the same time began to be mechanised the amount of equipment available from the UK in the crisis years from 1939 to 1941 was minimal, and most vehicles had therefore to come from the USA and Canada. Eventually most basic types were shipped Completely Knocked Down (CKD) and assembled in India, mostly with locally built bodies. Some CMP vehicles were assembled in Australia and shipped to India from there. Having established a supply route to China via Burma the USA had by 1942 a readymade pipeline for military supplies and this was augmented under Lend-Lease in order to equip the British and Indian Armies.

Before the war the rate of mechanisation of the Indian Army was far behind that of the British but recovery was provided for using vehicles of similar design to those in British Army use. Types used by IAOC and later IEME included Morris Commercial D Type 30-cwts with Harvey Frost cranes, Albion 3-ton 6×4 lorries with recovery cranes similar to the RASC pattern Weaver crane and, later, some Scammell Pioneers. The Cranes 7½-ton Light Recovery Trailer had also been supplied to India in 1938. British forces in both Burma and Malaya in the early war years were equipped with the standard recovery vehicles of the period.

*One of many jeep recovery modifications. This one in India.*

The reinforcements sent in 1941 and early 1942 brought more equipment but by that time few of the newer recovery vehicles had become available. The one Advanced Base Workshop in Malaya in 1941/42 could muster but one Leyland gantry lorry and a borrowed RASC breakdown lorry.

The retreat from Burma culminated in the loss of all the vehicles of the British forces there. New supplies were received from the UK but most new recovery vehicles used thereafter came from the USA or Canada. These included the Mack LMSW, Diamond T 969 and Ward La France wreckers already described. The Canadian Chevrolet and Ford CMP recovery vehicles were also widely used in Burma and India. The appalling conditions in the North Burma jungles meant that vehicles without 4- or 6-wheel drive were often barely able to move, especially in the mud of the monsoon season. Narrow trails often precluded the use of vehicles larger than Jeeps. The US and Canadian Dodge ¾-ton 4×4 and US 1½-ton 6×6 trucks were most useful in these conditions and for Operation ZIPPER, an all-Jeep and ¾-ton vehicle fleet was specified.

*Standard Canadian Military Pattern light recovery vehicle. Chevrolet 3-ton chassis and Garwood recovery gear.*

*A Mack NM tractor with Scammell 20-ton transporter semi-trailer photographed in Singapore in about 1948.*

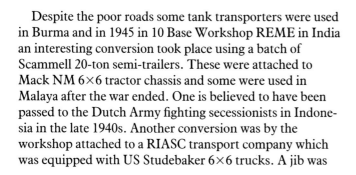

*A locally modified four wheeled truck of unknown make carrying an Indian Army Vickers Light Tank.*

Despite the poor roads some tank transporters were used in Burma and in 1945 in 10 Base Workshop REME in India an interesting conversion took place using a batch of Scammell 20-ton semi-trailers. These were attached to Mack NM 6×6 tractor chassis and some were used in Malaya after the war ended. One is believed to have been passed to the Dutch Army fighting secessionists in Indonesia in the late 1940s. Another conversion was by the workshop attached to a RIASC transport company which was equipped with US Studebaker 6×6 trucks. A jib was built from steel girders in the back of a winch-equipped truck which was retained as a recovery vehicle to the end of the war.

The official REME War Report for South East Asia states that no ARVs were used there. Only unarmoured tractors and wheeled recovery vehicles were available for tank recovery. During this time, however, an ARV was developed in Australia based on the US M3 Medium Tank but fitted with a winch and spade anchor. Other Australian experimental vehicles included recovery Jeeps.

# Part 4
# The Development of Recovery Vehicles Since 1945

# Chapter 1
# The Post–War Situation: The 1940s and 1950s

The surrender of Japan in August 1945 brought to an end the second and most catastrophic global war in living memory. It did not bring to an end the deployment of British troops overseas since they were still needed as occupation forces, as a counter to guerillas or simply to provide a measure of control pending the re-establishment of peacetime colonial government.

Despite Lend-Lease aid from the USA, the war had come close to bankrupting Britain and so the Treasury was quick to revert to peacetime accounting after six years of being forced to afford whatever was necessary for national survival. With the arrival of peace, the overriding need was for repair and renewal in Britain and the war-wracked parts of the Empire. There was also the need to give aid to Europe whilst at the same time paying off debts caused by the war. These considerations resulted inevitably in a long period of austerity. Financing the armed forces at this time came in for very close scrutiny and the using up of wartime stocks seemed a means of saving defence funds, echoing the situation after World War I. This may well have been sound economics for consumables but for equipment it took little account of several factors relevant to the wartime military vehicle fleet.

Most vehicles were well worn and required frequent and expensive overhauls. Some designs had been accepted for reasons of expediency rather than suitability. US-built equipment originally provided free or cheaply had now to be maintained with expensive imported spares. The re-creation of the TA, with its annual training exercises, quickly used up stocks of fit vehicles as did the continued presence of vast numbers of British troops overseas. These commitments were to be extended by the Malayan emergency, the beginning of preparations for atomic weapons tests and the need to reinforce the occupation force in Germany, the British Army of the Rhine (BAOR), as the 'cold war' began.

Besides the sheer numbers of military vehicles held at the end of the war and the lack of funds, another factor inhibiting new purchases was the need to export as much as possible of the motor industry's output in order to help pay for essential imports of food and raw materials. The Army struggled on with its old vehicle fleet with some pre-war vehicles surviving well into the 1950s and wartime vehicles much later. REME resources in the UK and in base workshops overseas were largely devoted to keeping an ageing fleet operational in defiance of what today would seem sound economics.

The Ministry of Supply (MOS) was by 1945 well established as a logistic support organisation for the War Office. In consultation with the Army, various equipment development projects were axed as the war ended but others were continued against a need to keep abreast of new design and technology and in the knowledge that wartime equipment would not last forever. The MOS retrenchments included in 1952 the combining of A and B Vehicle design and trials work at one establishment. The former A Vehicle centre at Chertsey, FVPE, and the design establishment (FVDE) combined with WVEE to become the Fighting Vehicles Research and Development Establishment (FVRDE). REME presence continued at MOS establishments with the role of influencing designs so that repair work would be simplified. For a time this influence was to be too weak and some vehicles accepted by the War Office were to be notoriously difficult to repair. The influence on recovery vehicle design was more effective since these were primarily REME operated. The concept by which a separate Ministry was responsible for the design, development and provision of the Army's equipment might be thought an unnecessary luxury once the war ended, but by tradition, civilian ministries, once created, are difficult to disestablish. The MOS survived and at times was retitled and given different roles and responsibilities. It continued to be the design and procurement agency for the Army until 1960 when these functions were, together with staff and technical establishments, transferred to the War Office, restoring to it at last what it had lost in 1939.

Another relevant reorganisation during this period was Phase II of the formation of REME. The Corps now absorbed most of the unit tradesmen and workshops which had continued throughout the war to be part of the corps and regiments operating equipment. Now the RASC transport company workshop platoons became REME LADs and workshops and the existing LADs with armoured and artillery regiments were increased in size, some of the regimental tradesmen taking the opportunity to transfer to REME.

New developments, both by MOS establishments and within the commercial vehicle industry, had rendered many wartime vehicles obsolete. The difficulty of maintaining them increased as spares were used up. The need to react to the Cold War had led to the continued production of Centurion tanks and small purchases of essential B Vehicles: it also led to the longer-term development of other new A and B Vehicles. The start of the Korean War in 1950 and the hardening of Russian attitudes gave some impetus to the renewal of the Army's vehicle fleet. Initial British vehicle deployment in Korea was, with the exception of the Centurion, entirely of World War II types. These included many vehicles of pre-war design if not manufacture. New designs emerging from the FVRDE and the motor industry were now hastened but few post-war vehicles were to be deployed in Korea before the 1953 ceasefire.

Before and during World War II each new tank design was given an A number. No similar numbering system was given to B Vehicles, though WVEE allocated trials numbers, but when the war ended and after the concentration of vehicle experimental work at Chertsey, a system of FV numbers was started and applied to all vehicle designs. A series number was given to those types which would be likely to result in a variety of sub-types. New equipment described hereafter quotes the FV number where this is known. Some equipment went into service without a name and has only ever been known by its FV number. This practice is more common with US equipment which is allocated an M number. Some of these are used by the British Army.

Many decisions on equipment policy made in 1944 and 1945 were, it was realised, unlikely to reach fruition in the short term but no one then knew how long the war would last. One scheme sought a greater level of standardisation in equipment, a field in which Britain showed up badly compared with some other countries. The first step was to produce a range of engines designed round a common cylinder size giving 4-, 6- and 8-cylinder variants with many other common components. These were developed by Rolls Royce and trials of the three types, B40, B60 and B80, in a variety of mainly World War II type vehicles, commenced in the late 1940s. The new-generation vehicles which would use these engines were to have many other common components and were to be deep wadeproofed with engine electrics suppressed to prevent radio interference. Some of the range were to have 24-volt electrical systems at a time when many foreign civilian vehicles were still being built with only 6-volt systems. The complexity and thus cost of these vehicles compared unfavourably with that of the basic wartime vehicles and the simpler cross-country vehicles being sold commercially by manufacturers. At the same time the post-war Army used vast numbers of domestic vehicles for the movement of stores, household fuel,

soldiers and families. There was clearly no need for these vehicles to be expensive types with an off-road capability. Therefore, in 1949, as the new post-war vehicles were being developed, a War Office policy statement decreed that there would be three classes of military B vehicle:

– The combat (CT) range: standardised vehicles with B series engines and all the other refinements described above.
– The General Service (GS) range: commercially designed vehicles, usually with all-wheel-drive but with manufacturers' own engines, military bodies and single rear wheels with cross-country tyres, fitments for crew weapons etc.
– The Civilian (CL) range: purely commercial vehicles, possibly modified to the extent of fitting weapon clips in the cab and in some cases military style bodies.

The concept envisaged that the CT range would equip all front-line units, the GS range would be used by supporting units and the CL range by base installations and as domestic vehicles in the UK training organisation. In practice this did not happen. Some of the CT range never reached production: most of them proved to be only a little better than the cheaper GS range which was found to be perfectly adequate for most purposes in fighting units.

The CT concept gradually faded but in its place the next generation of GS vehicles was far more complex with more FVRDE design input. This was partly due to a new idea in the late 1950s that all front-line military vehicles should have multi-fuel diesel engines, (see page 81). This led to the development of the L60 vertically opposed piston engine for the Chieftain tank and to a diesel development of one of the B series spark ignition (petrol) engines for smaller A vehicles.

The designation of wheeled vehicles had undergone a change at about the end of the war. Borrowing from the Americans it became the norm to refer to all types as trucks, regardless of size. The use of the word 'lorry' began to die out. For a time heavy recovery vehicles retained the designation 'tractor' but this soon became reserved for those vehicles intended primarily for pulling trailers or semi-trailers.

Some time after the war ended, the ERS REME was absorbed into the Maintenance Techniques Development Establishment (MTDE) REME. Experimental work continued and a hinged spade anchor was designed for the Austin gantry in 1950. MTDE then moved to Bordon, where its role is covered now by the School of Electrical and Mechanical Engineering (SEME).

# Chapter 2
# Recovery Vehicles and Transporters in the 1940s and 1950s

The first new development stemmed from wartime trials of a 6×6 version of the Scammell Pioneer gun tractor. Scammell Lorries Ltd of Watford produced a new prototype based on the Pioneer Heavy Recovery Tractor but with a set back, driven front axle, and after trials the new tractor was introduced in 1950. This was given the maker's name Explorer and FV number 11301. It used a Meadows 10.3-litre 6-cylinder petrol engine and its body and recovery gear closely resembled the earlier 6×4 vehicle. This all-wheel-drive Scammell had an excellent cross-country performance. Its 15-ton main winch and powered jib winch made it a very capable recovery vehicle and it was also much faster than its predecessor.

Despite the overall large surplus of wartime vehicles there was a severe shortage of heavy recovery vehicles which

continued into the 1960s. Many units were issued with medium recovery vehicles instead and some static workshops and TA units were provided with Scammell Pioneer artillery tractors to be used for recovery. The justification for purchasing the new Scammell was greatly increased by the outbreak of the Korean War. By 1951 the first of the new Scammells were being issued to REME units and by the time of the ceasefire in 1953 some of them were at work in Korea. A number of those built during the next few years went to the RAF.

Relatively few modifications were made to the Scammell 6×6 recovery vehicle during its long service life: however, the Mark 2 appeared with its front towing hook on a solid cross beam instead of on a leaf sprung mounting. Some, but not all, used in Korea were fitted with cab insulation to

*The Scammell Explorer demonstrating that six-wheel drive does not solve all problems.*

*A curious conversion. Originally a Scammell Pioneer gun tractor this was fitted with the jib and counter weights from a breakdown tractor but retained the gun tractor's steel body.*

counter the extreme cold of the Korean winter and others in East Africa had additional air intakes fitted to the roof to help cool the cab. A small number of these vehicles was fitted with folding rear spades and others carried special towing gear for the Centurion tank's mono-wheel fuel trailer. Some of the RAF Explorers were subsequently transferred to the Army which was eventually to employ a total of over 600. A few Explorers with commercial pattern cabs were exported to New Zealand for RNZEME and a much larger number of similar vehicles was purchased by the Egyptian Army.

The new Scammells issued during the early 1950s displaced the older Pioneer 6×4 vehicles, which were then redeployed to units which had been forced to manage with 3-ton breakdown gantry lorries. After Regular units were re-equipped any surplus Pioneers were transferred to TA units or training pools. Many old soldiers still preferred the simpler, plodding diesel version, which remains to this day something like a cherished family pet within REME. In the last two decades an increasing number of Scammell 6×6 Explorers have been sold off and for some years could be

seen on the forecourts of civilian garages still in use.

Within the framework of the CT vehicle concept a number of recovery variants were proposed. What had been planned as a 3-ton 6×6 range of vehicles was later upgraded to a 5-ton load capacity. A few experimental chassis were built by Albion, Thornycroft and Vauxhall. WD numbers were allocated to recovery versions of the Albion and Thornycroft chassis, but there is no indication that any 5-ton 6×6 recovery vehicle was completed. One of the Albion chassis was shown at the 1956 British Military Vehicle Exhibition.

A parallel development in the 3-ton 4×4 GS range was a recovery vehicle initially classified as medium, but when plans for a projected 1-ton light recovery vehicle were dropped, the 3-tonner took the 'light' classification. The prototype was built on the Commer Q4 chassis, then being used for GS trucks, machinery lorries and RE tippers and was given the design number FV 13218. To support a suspended load of 4 tons the normal single rear wheels were replaced by twin rear wheels. The vehicle's chassis width made smaller tyres necessary in order to retain the standard overall vehicle width so the recovery version used 9.00×20 tyres instead of the 11.00×20 tyres used singly on most 3-tonners. The recovery gear resembled to some degree that of the wartime Ward La France (see Part 3), having a single swinging and elevating jib held in place by wire stays attached to a frame at the front of the body. A powered jib winch was fitted and a 5-ton chassis winch provided the main means of recovery. To give purchase when winching two detachable anchors or sprag legs were carried similar to those used on the experimental wartime Mack NM. The bodies of the prototypes were built by Mann Egerton Ltd.

After trials in the early 1950s with the Commer and an alternative vehicle on a similarly modified Bedford RL chassis (FV 13115), it was decided in 1955 to use the latter chassis for production vehicles. Bodies were built by

*Truck 3-ton Light Recovery Bedford RL photographed in Cyprus.*

Marshalls of Cambridge. A number of these vehicles were supplied to the Home Office for the post-war Auxiliary Fire Service. Some were also exported to New Zealand for RNZEME. British Army Bedfords, originally designated Tractor 3-ton GS Recovery Light, were issued during the 1960s to replace wartime Austin gantry lorries (see Part 3). About 160 Bedford recovery vehicles were built for the Army.

Like the earlier Scammell the Bedford was used throughout the world. When it originally entered service most WD vehicles were painted gloss Bronze Green. Before long a change was made to a matt green with random patches of black which quickly weathered to a dark grey. In the Middle East and Mediterranean a desert sand colour was used while those vehicles serving with the UN or earmarked for use in Norway were painted white.

Despite the arrival of the new Scammells in the 1950s many problems remained for REME workshops and recovery units. The surviving diesel Scammells were gradually wearing out but, more importantly, some of the newer vehicles being developed towards the end of the 1950s were beyond the recovery capacity of either Scammell. A recovery version of the 10-ton 6×6 class of the new CT range vehicles was therefore developed under the designation, Tractor 10-ton CT Heavy Recovery, Leyland (FV 1119). It was based on the chassis already used for the gun tractor but fitted with a more powerful winch. The Leyland was powered by a Rolls B Series B81 straight 8-cylinder petrol engine. The vehicle's transmission and suspension layout resembled that of the Scammell Explorer.

*Tractor CT Heavy Recovery 6×6 Leyland defeated by an ancient cannon. This lift was possible provided the rear stabilisers were used.*

Its recovery gear consisted of a 15-ton two-speed hydraulic chassis winch and an hydraulic crane mounted on a central pedestal with a crew seat and controls at one side. The basic design of the crane was similar to the Austin Western used on various US recovery vehicles. The great advantage of the vehicle's design was that it could be used for recovery or as a

*A Land Rover Mark 3 with recovery jib and steadying jacks.*

workshop crane. With the jib fixed in the rear position, supported by stays, lifts of up to 10 tons were possible when towing and 15 tons when stationary. The new vehicle was more complex than any recovery vehicle used up to that time. The original order was for 280 vehicles and they were deployed world-wide. In the Persian Gulf area the Leyland was fitted with wide, low-pressure sand tyres. In the UK, trials were conducted using a Leyland with open cage-like cylindrical extensions to the rear wheels to improve stability on hard surfaces in a crane role. The Leyland remains in service but is scheduled for replacement soon by newer-generation recovery vehicles. The introduction of the Leyland as a heavy recovery vehicle led to the downgrading of all Scammells to a medium classification. One Leyland was tested in Australia by RAEME but was not adopted.

The Leyland and Bedford designs took some years to progress through the MOS and War Office peace-time design, testing and production cycle. Other expedients had to be found to equip units during the early 1950s. At this time the USA was supplying Western European countries with military equipment under a 'Military Defence Aid Program' which sought to strengthen the armed forces of what was to become the North Atlantic Treaty Organisation (NATO). Among military vehicles supplied were numerous

*Berlin Workshop's Mercedes 3-ton 4×4 breakdown truck of the 1950s.*

refurbished ex-World War II recovery vehicles. BAOR qualified for some MDAP issues and 60 Diamond T 969 wreckers were obtained, most being disposed of with a handful of surviving wartime-issued US recovery vehicles within less than ten years.

By 1949 the Army was testing the new Land Rover and, despite the development of the Truck ¼-ton CT 4×4, the Austin Champ, Land Rovers were taken into service in the mid-1950s. Within a short time REME had adapted one as a recovery vehicle. A tubular steel A frame was attached to the rear, steadied by cables, and a portable winch carried. A light dummy axle of similar design to those used in the 1930s could be towed, taking the weight of one end of a light vehicle casualty. This equipment was adapted to fit later versions of the Land Rover and continued to provide the main means of recovery in airborne or airportable units.

Berlin is divided between four occupying powers, the British 'Berlin Brigade' being funded on a separate basis from BAOR. One result has long been the local provision of some vehicles and equipment. In the 1950s this led to the issue there of Mercedes 3-ton 4×4 recovery vehicles fitted with Bilstein cranes. In the Middle East, Italy (while British troops remained there) and in Austria some of the wartime recovery vehicles converted from US gun tractors survived into the early 1950s.

When the war ended new tank transporter trailers were under development to meet the needs of the new and heavier tanks coming into service. Trials continued with the 70-ton tilt-bed trailer to move the Tortoise tank destroyer, six of which were completed after the war and tested in BAOR. Other experimental trailers seem to have disappeared leaving the wartime 40-ton trailers, some strengthened and modified, and the first of the Cranes 50-ton trailers to carry the new Centurion. Later R.A. Dyson & Co of Liverpool developed an improved 50-ton version of the wartime 40-ton Mark 2 trailer; originally a Dyson design (see Part 3). The new trailer was similar in appearance and construction to the Cranes 50-ton design. The 50-ton trailers were about one foot wider than the earlier 40-tonners and could accept slight overloads, enabling them to cope with later, heavier Marks of Centurion. The FV number 3601 was allocated initially to the Dyson trailer design.

The only tractor available for the new trailers at first was the wartime Diamond T and over 1,200 of these continued in service, some for another two decades. Some were re-engined from 1956 to 1957 since spares for the American Hercules diesel engine became scarce and expensive. The new engine, a Rolls Royce C6 NFL diesel, resulted in a slight change to the external appearance of the tractor, the right-hand bonnet side panel being modified to accommodate the engine accessories. About 60 additional Diamond Ts are believed to have been received among MDAP allocations in the 1950s. These were 981s rebuilt with all steel cabs. The last Diamond T tractor was not replaced until 1975.

Chapter 3 includes details of the history and development of tanks in the FV 200 series of armoured vehicles, culminating in the 65-ton Conqueror Heavy Gun Tank (FV 214). To carry these tanks in the 60-ton plus weight range there was a need for a new transporter and it was intended that this should have a good cross-country performance. Experiments had been conducted with the American Pacific Tractor (see Part 3) and its performance led to the specification of 6-wheel drive for the tractor of the new vehicle. MOS also designed a semi-trailer (FV 3301), whose concessions to the needs of off-road movement made its practical use somewhat suspect.

The tractor was given the design number FV 1003 and a prototype was built by Leyland. It was fitted with twin rear tyres and as the tyre size was 18.00×24 the overall width of the vehicle was some 13 feet, as wide as the trailer itself and the tanks it would carry. The need for such a load-carrying capacity in the tractor was partly because of the design of the semi-trailer. The desired off-road performance led to the use of the same massive tyres on the trailer and the eight wheels were mounted on four stub axles, one on each end of two unsprung walking beams. To allow for articulation of the rear bogies the trackways above the wheels were over 7 feet from the ground necessitating two three-section folding rear ramps. To lower the centre of gravity of a laden trailer the trackways sloped downwards forward from the hump at the rear, the frame then sloping sharply upwards to the swan neck; thus a tank would be carried tilted forward, throwing more of its weight on to the tractor. The design progressed but foundered due to outside influences. The

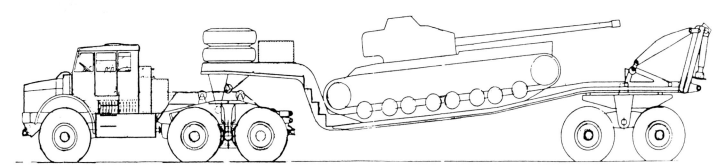

*A drawing of the proposed FV 1000 series 60-ton tank transporter. The Leyland tractor was built and tested with a short semi-trailer filled with ballast weights.*

RE had set an upper bridging limit of 100 tons and the FV 1003/3301 combination when laden with Conqueror was expected to exceed this limit by a considerable margin. Fortunately an interim solution to the problem of carrying FV 200 series tanks was at hand. The FV 1000 series was to have included FV 1001, a heavy tractor with ballast body, and FV 1004, a heavy recovery vehicle, but only the one FV 1003 was built. It was afterwards converted to a gradient simulation vehicle, being disposed of in 1976.

Soon after the war ended Messrs Thornycrofts of Basingstoke began development of a massive tractor primarily for use by oil companies in the Middle East. It was intended to tow semi-trailers or, in long wheelbase form, to carry loads of oil exploration equipment. The vehicle, known as the Mighty Antar, was tested by the MOS and in its tractor form it was adopted by the Army as a replacement for the Diamond T.

The first Antars in service in 1951 were tractors with fixed steel ballast bodies and were given the design number FV 12001. They could easily cope with the new 50-ton trailers. A 20-ton winch was fitted behind the cab for hauling dead tanks onto the trailer but for the early trials no winches were available so plans were made for adapting winches taken from Diamond T tractors. The new tractor dwarfed its predecessor which was essentially a large road-going vehicle. The Antar's official designation was Tractor 30-ton GS 6×4 and its width of 10ft 6ins was over 2 feet more than the American vehicle. The Antar's engine was a Rover-built Meteorite V8 petrol engine. This was, in effect, a sawn-off Meteor tank engine. Commercial versions of the Meteorite were available as diesels.

The Antar was further developed as a tractor for semi-trailer (FV 12002) and, following the scrapping of the FV 1000 series transporter, became the standard British Army transporter. FVDE, before its incorporation into FVRDE, produced a semi-trailer design capable of carrying the FV 200 series tanks. This trailer, FV 3001, had two rows of stub axles at the rear carrying a total of sixteen wheels. Its low horizontal trackways were reached via two folding rear ramps, tanks passing over a slight hump above the rear wheels and moving forward on the trailer so as to spread the weight more evenly between the tractor and trailer wheels. Later versions of this semi-trailer were designated FV 3005. The trailer frame sloped gently up at the front, giving adequate clearance under the hull of the transported tank, to the swan neck over the tractor's fifth wheel coupling. Folding legs were fitted under the trailer frame to enable it to stand detached from the tractor. Toolboxes were fixed under the trackways in production trailers and a small hoist over the swan neck could lift or lower the spare wheel. The smaller wheels and lower track-way made this a much more stable trailer. Trials of the Antar with the new semi-trailer took place from 1953 to 1955 and included a test run by 19 Tank Transporter Company RASC during July 1953. Another semi-trailer (FV 3011) of generally similar appearance to the 60-tonner but rated at 50 tons was adopted for carrying the more common Centurion tanks and other lighter armoured vehicles. FV 3011 featured a more sharply sloping frame up to the swan neck, smaller wheels and tyres and was slightly smaller than FV 3001. Both trailers were built by Joseph Sankey Ltd to start with but subsequently the 50-tonners were also built by GKN and Taskers.

*The Thornycroft Antar with steel ballast body and a Dyson trailer. A Centurion tank is being driven on board.*

Later versions of the Antar Mark 1 were built with a timber ballast body for use as tractors for the 50-ton Dyson trailer but could be converted simply to tractors for the 60-ton semi-trailer.

Following the development of the FV 1000 tractor, sometimes named the Brontosaurus, another range of heavy tractors 30-ton CT was proposed under the series heading FV 1200. Original design work was undertaken in 1950 by Dennis Brothers of Guildford, the firm more renowned for fire engines. After accepting an MOS contract, carrying out research and preparing drawings the company found it could not expand its factory sufficiently to carry out production of the new range which would have included a heavy gun tractor, a heavy tractor for a tank transporter and a heavy recovery vehicle. MOS arranged in 1953 to transfer the work to Leyland Motors but only a few FV 1200 series Leylands were built. One with a prototype gun tractor body, FV 1201, was used in 1955 and 1956 for trials as a tank tractor echoing wartime trials with a 6×6 Scammell Pioneer. FV 1200 vehicles featured 6-wheel drive, Meteorite engines and huge 18.00×24 single tyres. The cost and size of these machines was the probable reason for their demise. Parts of one of them survived in a scrapyard in 1987.

The advantage of a full trailer for carrying smaller vehicle casualties has always been that any suitable prime mover could pull it rather than a specialist tractor. For this reason a number of small transporters have been developed and some commercial trailers adopted by the Army over the years.

*The Leyland FV 1201 Heavy Tractor being tested towing a Conqueror Heavy Gun Tank. A Centurion ARV Mark 1 is on the left.*

The earliest post-war trailer for this role was a replacement for the pre-war designed Cranes 7½-ton light recovery trailer. The new trailer (FV 3221) was rated at 10 tons and intended for carrying FV 600 series wheeled armoured vehicles (Saracen and Saladin), FV 400 vehicles, the last of the open-topped tracked carriers, and B vehicles. The FV 430 series carriers including FV 432 (see Chapter 4) could be carried when the trailer was later modified. The trailer, on two axles, featured a front turntable and each axle carried two twin wheels. Detachable ramps for loading were carried between the track-ways. The trailer was developed and built by Rubery Owen in the 1950s but did not finally enter service until 1960. Some production trailers were built by J. Brockhouse.

The FVRDE and its successors have always tested commercial vehicles which might have some potential for military employment. During the 1950s a new name in heavy haulage tractors was Rotinoff. The Rotinoff Atlantic 6×4 tractor was aimed at filling the same role as the Diamond T 980/981 and the new Thornycroft Antar. An Atlantic with Rolls C6 diesel engine was tested as a tractor in 1954/55 and was used with the FV 3001 60-ton semi-trailer. A year or so later the vehicle was tested again, this time as a ballast tractor with single rear wheels and towing the FV 3601 50-ton trailer. Rotinoff then produced a Super Atlantic and a version was tested in 1960 with an AEC engine. This vehicle was also tried with a 60-ton semi-trailer. No production Rotinoffs were to be used by the British Army but Switzerland purchased some as tank transporters.

Two other vehicles taken into use by the Army in the 1950s were versions of a commercial 6×6 Scammell developed for oilfield work and heavy haulage. The Scammell Constructor was a big vehicle but much smaller than the Antar. The two versions first issued were mainly for the RE. The 20-ton ballast bodied tractor usually hauled the drop frame trailers commonly used for carrying tracked RE plant, dozers, excavators etc. The tractor chassis used three separate axles rather than the rear transmission system of the Explorer but shared the latter's Meadows petrol engine. The cab was very narrow in relation to the size of

*The Rotinoff Atlantic commercial heavy tractor being tested with the 60-ton semi-trailer normally fitted to the Thornycroft Antar.*

the vehicle and used pressings from a former Bedford truck model. A timber ballast body was fitted. Tyres were 12.00×20, twin on the rear axles. The overall width was about the same as that of the Explorer. Although not designed as a tank transporter this vehicle was quite capable of hauling smaller armoured vehicles on trailers. Its 15-ton winch gave it a useful recovery capacity if needed.

The other Constructor was a 20-ton tractor for a 30-ton semi-trailer for RE plant. The tractor chassis was similar to the one described but was fitted with a Rolls Royce C6 NFL diesel engine. Larger tyres were fitted, 14.00×20 still twinned on rear axles resulting in a vehicle 8 inches wider than the ballast tractor. The Taskers 30-ton drop-frame semi-trailer (FV 3541), used very small 10.00×15 tyres on its two rear rows of wheels so it was possible to build it with a flat floor. A two-piece folding full-width rear ramp simplified the loading of plant of any size or width. The trailer was 10 ft 6 ins wide and could therefore carry quite large armoured vehicles if need be.

An unladen Thornycroft Antar weighed about 20 tons and no in-service recovery vehicle could lift one end of the vehicle to provide a suspended tow. This was one reason why super-heavy recovery variants of the FV 1000 and FV 1200 series of vehicles were contemplated. Something was needed more quickly. In about 1952 a RASC officer in a tank transporter company devised a bolt-on jib which could be fitted to an Antar tractor enabling it to tow another suspended Antar. The device was not officially approved for quantity production so the problem remained. Instead it was decided to build a recovery dolly, or dummy axle capable of taking the weight of either end of the Antar. The logic of this idea can be seen when considering the cost of developing a superheavy recovery vehicle solely to cover the relatively small number of times when an Antar would need a suspended tow: however the dummy axle with jib did not enter service until many years later.

The need for heavy tractors to pull trailers in the 20-ton class, mostly for RE equipment, had to be met while the Scammell Constructors were being developed and built. There were a number of ex-RA heavy tractors, Scammell Pioneer and Albion CX22S and a small number of US types but a ballast-bodied tractor was considered more useful. There were at this time a lot of surplus Scammell transporters so the tractors from these were converted, starting in 1953 at 27 Command Workshop REME. Above the fifth wheel coupling a steel frame was built onto which concrete blocks were stacked. A small jib at the rear enabled the spare wheel to be lifted or lowered to the ground.

The majority of infantry battalions in the 1950s and 1960s were semi-mechanised, that is, with domestic transport but dependent on the provision of additional troop carriers to move as one whole unit. To provide the few REME soldiers maintaining the battalion's vehicles with a means for recovery, one or more 3-ton cargo trucks were issued fitted with chassis winches. A World War II vehicle which survived for many years in this role was the Karrier K 6. It was superseded in the late 1950s by the Bedford RL 3-ton truck with winch (FV 13105).

*A row of Scammell Pioneer tank transporter tractors converted to ballast bodied tractors for full trailers.*

*The demountable recovery jib designed for the Thornycroft Antar by the RASC.*

# Chapter 3
# The First Post-War ARVs

The ARV situation in the last two years of World War II was described in Part 3. The majority available were Mark I types without winches. A relatively small number of Mark 2 Churchills and Shermans and some M32 Shermans were in use. For many workshops the Caterpillar D8 tractor continued to be the main tank recovery vehicle assisted by the Diamond T tractor and Scammells. Fortunately the rapid run-down in the size of the Army enabled the best use to be made of Mark IIs in armoured workshops and tank regiments but there were still too few and the scale of issue of all types of ARV was frequently below entitlement. For a long time RA Regiments with self-propelled guns had no ARVs. A December 1954 report proposed the issue of Ram ARVs and some RA regiment LADs received Shermans. TA units were lucky to get any ARVs for training and some were expected to manage with turretless Stuart M5 light tanks with such recovery gear as could be stowed on board.

With the end of the war and the subsequent demise of the Experimental Recovery Section REME, the responsibility for ARV design reverted to the MOS but, although designs were produced in the five years after VJ Day, little practical work was possible, given the greater priority for developing the new Centurion gun tank and designing its successor. Whilst still a useful ARV during the war, the Churchill by 1950 was so underpowered and slow that its effectiveness in battle was questioned. Its drawbacks were to become all too evident in the Korean War.

Russia's last minute declaration of war in 1945 on a Japan by then already very weakened after nearly fourteen years of war against China and four years against the Allies, gave the communist giant a relatively easy victory. Japanese forces in northern China, and Korea, which had long been a Japanese colony, were close to defeat by the time the emperor decided to sue for peace after the two atomic bombs had been dropped. In the post-war 'carve up' of the Japanese colonies and outer islands Russian forces occupied North Korea and US forces South Korea. The dividing line for convenience was the 38th parallel as it bisected the country. The intention was supposed to be a return to a single elected Korean government but the dividing line soon became an international boundary as North Korea set up its own communist government claiming to represent the whole country.

By 1950 the US occupation forces had been reduced to a lightly armed token force and a new Republic of Korea

*Korea. A Scammell Pioneer heads a train of Scammell Explorer and Diamond T with 50-ton Dyson trailer carrying a Centurion ARV Mark 1. Four recovery vehicles for the price of one.*

(ROK) (South Korean) army was slowly being developed. At this point the North Korean army, a larger and more mechanised force, was launched across the 38th parallel and occupied almost the whole country. The surviving ROK forces and the one US Army Infantry Division were holding a small bridgehead around the harbour of Pusan when a United Nations resolution called for all nations to join in combatting the North Korean aggression. As US Army reinforcements were rushed from Japan and the USA, Britain took up the UN call and dispatched units from Hong Kong and the UK. These were soon followed by contingents from Canada, Australia, New Zealand and India, which were later to form a Commonwealth Division. The subsequent defeat of North Korea followed by the intervention of Communist China and reversals for the UN and ROK forces finally led to a cease-fire and truce in 1953 which remains the official situation today.

The Centurion tank was to be first used in action in Korea. By 1950 the Mark 3 version of the tank was in service; weighing in fighting trim about 52 tons, it scaled 10 tons more than the heaviest British tank to see war service up to 1945. An urgent need therefore arose for an improved ARV. As an interim solution some damaged Centurions were converted to turretless tractors similar in concept to the Mark I ARVs of 1942. The Centurion 'tugs' were converted in the Commonwealth Base Workshop at Kure, Japan. This had been set up originally in 1945 to provide repair support to the Commonwealth occupation forces, but by 1950 those were almost entirely Australian. With the start of the war in neighbouring Korea this workshop was boosted by a large REME contingent but remained a RAEME unit.

The tugs in Korea were not only used for recovery but also as supply and ammunition carriers to exposed positions. The Centurion, with its Meteor engine, had a remarkable hill-climbing ability which was enhanced without the weight of the turret, thus making it an invaluable piece of equipment. For recovery, however, it suffered from all the same drawbacks as its 1942 ancestors and so a proper ARV with a winch on the Centurion hull was urgently sought. This led to the building during 1951 in 13 Command Workshop REME at Aldershot of a prototype Centurion ARV followed rapidly by ten production versions. These were designated Centurion ARV Mark 1. At the same time MOS set about the 'official' design of a Centurion ARV which would become the Mark 2.

The Mark 1 drew heavily on Churchill Mark 2 technology and some of its components were similar, the prototype actually using Churchill components. It was not possible to take the drive from the main engine as in the Churchill so a Bedford truck engine had to be squeezed into the winch and crew compartment. The dummy turret resembled that of the Churchill but was newly built for the Centurion. A set of the original drawings for the conversion is held in the REME Museum. The need for a separate winch engine resulted in a very confined space for the crew and most major maintenance to the winch involved removing the turret top access hatches and working from the outside. The Mark 1 ARV was fitted with an 18-ton winch and extensive recovery tackle layouts were required to achieve the pulls necessary for major winching tasks. Very little enclosed stowage space was provided for the hundred and one devices and stores needed for recovery and this was to be corrected in the Mark 2.

The first eleven Centurion ARVs Mark 1, including the prototype, were completed by the end of 1951. Eight were sent to Korea arriving in March 1952, two to BAOR and one remained in UK for training. Work soon began on a further batch, hulls for which were provided by withdrawing more of the Centurion tugs. The first reports from Korea suggested the need for improved access to the crew compartment and called for vision devices for the vehicle commander to enable him to control the tank when it was closed down. In general the new ARV was recognised as a vast improvement on the Churchill. The next batch of REME-built ARVs was modified to correct faults and altogether over 170 conversions were made between 1951 and 1957. Six of the Mark 1s were later moved from Korea to the Middle East and the bulk of the later-built examples went to BAOR. Some Mark 1s remained in service till the early 1960s then finished their days as recovery training hulks or hard targets.

*An early Centurion ARV Mark 1 winching a Churchill hulk using a two to one pull.*

*An early Centurion tank 'tug' in BAOR.*

*Centurion ARV Mark 2 showing the rear spade anchor and recovery mechanics pulling out the winch rope and setting up a snatch block for a two to one pull.*

Whilst 'tugs' had been built in Japan for use in Korea the same idea had taken root in Europe but these were intended purely as interim recovery vehicles. Mark 1, 2 and 3 tanks were modified at 27 Command Workshop for UK and in 7 Armoured Workshop for BAOR. The turret was removed but the traverse gear was retained and used to rotate a drum-shaped cable reel on the turret ring. This was simply a device for stowing the cable and was in no way capable of being used as a recovery winch. These Centurion tugs, like those in Korea, had no means of unditching badly bogged tanks other than by towing. Their advantages were speed into action and commonality of design with the gun tanks they supported.

The MOS designed ARV Mark 2 (FV 4006) had its teething problems and testing of the prototype, 03ZR52, led to radical redesign work and thus to delays, trials continuing until 1954. The layout of the vehicle was similar to that of the Mark 1 but the winch and crew housing was slightly larger. Drive to the 30-ton winch was provided by an electric motor and current was generated using a Rolls-designed B81 engine. This more complex equipment further reduced the crew space. Access to the winch for some maintenance tasks involved removing the roof. In addition to winching to the rear, the main winch rope could be routed to the right or left of the vehicle pulling up to 20 tons or it could be fed round a pulley at the rear and over the turret roof to winch to the front. This was primarily intended for using a crane jib which was provided for the ARV but rarely used since it had to be carried on a separate vehicle. Provision was made for using a heavy timber prop when 'pushing' with the ARV. Lockers were fitted to both sides of the vehicle and on the front of the crew compartment. It became the practice in some BAOR units to provide a crew shelter under canvas in the well over the engine deck and between the side lockers. This was fine until an engine fault resulted in a need to lift the engine covers. A much more substantial spade anchor was designed for the Mark 2 ARV resembling that used on the wartime German Panther ARV. As on the Mark 1 this was raised or lowered using the main winch cable. Production of Mark 2 ARVs was started by Vickers in 1955 and initially hulls were provided by using old tank tugs or early marks of gun tank. In addition to those built for the Army many were exported.

The first came into service in 1956 and many were still in service in 1988.

Few major modifications were to be carried out to the Mark 2 but one resulted in a number of BAOR examples having their locker layouts changed to enable them to carry spare L7 105mm tank gun barrels so that ones worn out could be changed in the field. The intention was to save transporting the barrels, weighing over a ton, on trucks or trailers and thus to reduce the number of vehicles needed for the process. The concept, however, fell into disuse because the ARV was not equipped to carry out the barrel change itself since, even if the crane attachment originally provided had been used, it was in the wrong place to be able to lift the gun barrels from their positions at the side of the vehicle. In practice a half-track fitters vehicle or the FV 434 Carrier Full Tracked Maintenance or some wheeled recovery vehicle was needed to lift the barrel from the ARV. Once the Chieftain came into service using a longer and heavier gun the idea was dropped entirely and some ARVs had their locker layouts restored to the original design.

Most countries which purchased Centurion tanks also bought a number of ARVs so the combat operations of the Centurion ARV Mark 2 have an international history. RAEME used the vehicle in Vietnam and others are believed to have been used in various Middle East wars. A proposed Centurion ARV Mark 3 would, like the Conqueror Mark 2 and Chieftain, have had the hull glacis plate continued to form the front of the winch and crew compartment, placing the driver in with the rest of the crew. This variant did not materialise as a Centurion. The Centurion tank, A41, was developed in 1944/45 as a heavy cruiser tank and, as a complementary infantry tank, an even bigger vehicle was produced under the designation A45.

In 1946 the War Office published its plans for future tank development: the Centurion (A41) would become a Universal Tank dispensing with the separate cruiser and infantry tank concepts. It would also form the basis for many specialist A vehicles, most of which had originally been built on the Churchill hull. Doubts were soon cast on the suitability of the Centurion for some of the specialist roles so it was decided to replace it with a heavier universal tank. The series was allocated the design number FV 200 and was based on the earlier A45. Plans for a range of vehicles on a common hull were soon scrapped when it was found that some equipment would not fit and in some cases a complete vehicle was too big for standard landing craft. The new universal tank was therefore discarded and the development of Centurion proceeded. In practice it was soon clear that the Centurion could in fact accommodate most of the specialist equipment, confounding the earlier doubters. The new FV 200 series A vehicle development did however continue, a few hulls being fitted with Centurion turrets and given the name Caernarvon. These were used for trials, including two being tested in Libya, while work continued on the first of the few vehicles in the FV 200 series which were destined to go into production.

There had long been a fear that no in-service tank or anti-tank weapon could defeat the armour of the Soviet heavy tank Joseph Stalin III. To restore the balance a heavy gun tank was developed based on the FV 200 hull and with a cast turret mounting an American designed 120mm gun. This eventually emerged as Conqueror (FV 214). An ARV for the series had been planned as FV 209 and development

was cancelled in 1951 with the main universal tank concept. The ARV was then revived as the support vehicle for Conqueror and in view of the changed specification was given a new number, FV 219. The Conqueror ARV Mark 1 was in layout similar to the Centurion with a fixed box structure to house winch and crew in place of the rotating turret of the gun tank. The driver sat in the hull as in the gun tank. The winch, with a direct pull of 45 tons, was driven by the main engine, which was a fuel-injected development of the Meteor giving a greatly increased power output. A hinged rear spade provided an anchor when winching. Small equipment could be carried in the stowage bins on each side of the winch housing. Also carried, in sections, was a small box girder jib which could be fitted to the spade supported by stays for use as a rear crane. A long development period preceded acceptance for issue in 1959, which was a few years after the gun tanks were deployed. A year later the first Mark 2 version was undergoing trials at Bordon. This version used a revised hull layout similar to the projected Centurion ARV Mark 3 with the driver seated in the main crew and winch compartment. It was given the design number FV 222, and mechanically it was similar to the Mark 1.

The few Conqueror ARVs were well received because the power of the winch enabled many recovery tasks to be accomplished with a straight pull thus avoiding the need to

*Conqueror ARV Mark 2, perhaps one of the best ARVs ever produced.*

set up complex layouts of snatch blocks and cable. Like all the Conquerors, the ARV proved difficult to transport because of its width, nearly 2 feet more than Centurion. When the Conqueror's short reign ended in 1966 a few ARVs were retained, one Mark 2 eventually being returned from BAOR for the REME Museum collection. A Mark 1 survived to move targets on the ranges at Shoeburyness and may yet be rescued for preservation.

At the other end of the scale a new light tank series was being developed in the war years designated A46; revived in 1946 under the FV number 300, its proposed ARV variant was FV 306. The contemporary development of the new 6-wheeled Saladin armoured car, and the Saracen armoured personnel carrier (APC) may have led to the cancellation of the FV 300 series since a quite heavy gun, 76mm, could be fitted to the Saladin which weighed only about half as much

*The experimental wheeled recovery vehicle based on a Ferret Scout Car. The design was radically altered in later experiments.*

as the light tank. A series of amphibious cargo carriers, similar in appearance to the US LVT (Buffalo or Fantail), was developed during the war under the name Neptune. Development continued after the war under FV number 500 and a recovery variant FV 503 was proposed.

Some measure of local improvisation continued after the war especially in overseas theatres. Armoured car equipped reconnaissance units have always suffered from the lack of a recovery vehicle which would give REME tradesmen some protection in recovery operations under fire. In Malaya some improvised armoured cabs appeared on recovery vehicles but in general the LADs depended on escorting Scout cars or went without. As a result some REME soldiers died in terrorist ambushes.

Faced a few years earlier with a similar guerilla enemy the Life Guards in Palestine developed a wheeled ARV which was in essence a turretless AEC armoured car. It was used simply as a tug having no winch. It did at least provide crew protection. The unit later moved to BAOR and, together with its LAD, developed the idea further using another AEC, this time with an internally mounted powered winch,

rear jib and a rotating armoured cover over the turret ring. Only one was built despite its reported success. The imminent replacement of the AEC and Daimler Armoured Cars in the regiment by Saladins may explain the demise of this promising design. In 1953 EME Branch at the War Office reported proposals for a wheeled ARV based on the Saracen but there is no indication that any designs were completed.

By the late 1950s the wartime Sherman Beach ARV needed replacing. The obvious solution was to use the hull of the current main battle tank, the Centurion. A design was produced by Fording Trials Branch REME based on the superstructure shape used on the Sherman. A mock-up was built and then a prototype with a mild steel upper hull, based on a Centurion tug. It was demonstrated at Instow then taken to FVRDE for trials in 1960. By the end of that year the entire production batch of twelve had been completed at the Royal Ordnance Factory (ROF) Leeds.

Like its predecessor the Centurion BARV had no winch but relied on pushing or direct pulls to unstick drowned vehicles or beached landing craft. These vehicles were based

*The Centurion Beach ARV being used for landing craft loading trials.*

on Mark 3 hulls and the superstructure of production vehicles was in armour plate. The BARV could wade up to 9ft 6ins. In shallow water the driver had direct vision through an armoured glass vision block: in deeper water he was dependent on directions from the vehicle commander. A set of lifting gear was designed for the BARV which could be attached to the hull and could lift out its own engine for repairs, reminiscent of the wartime Atherton turret hoist. A BARV was carried on the major assault landing ships and others were used at Instow. Later, as the amphibious role was passed to the Royal Marines, the Centurion BARVs were also handed over. Two Centurion BARVs accompanied the British forces to the Falkland Islands in 1982.

In 1955 a Churchill tank was tested in a BARV role by the RE. This was a sealed hull with a tall cylindrical tower over the turret ring. Nothing more is known of this experiment. As wartime trials had tested and discarded the Churchill in this role it is not known what prompted a second attempt.

During World War II the close cooperation between Britain and Canada on vehicle design and production led to the Canadian Snomobile oversnow vehicle being adopted for the British Army for use in Arctic warfare, since planning had to cover the possibility of a campaign to drive the Germans out of Norway. Very few Snomobiles were delivered before the war ended. After extensive trials of vehicles on the Canadian tundra during 1946, known as the Camp Churchill project, a proposal was made in UK for an ARV variant of the armoured Snomobile. Nothing further has been discovered on this proposal.

By the end of the 1950s the concept of repairing tanks *in situ* and the expected short duration of a future war removed the need for much backloading to workshops. The remaining work of this sort was passed to the RASC tank transporter companies and REME's operation of the heavier transporters thereafter was limited to a few in workshops for the carriage of ARVs.

*Experimental AEC armoured car based ARV.*

# Chapter 4
# The 1960s: New Philosophies and New Designs

The 1950s ended with the 'Cold War' at an intense stage and with BAOR taking a considerable proportion of the Army's resources. At the same time there remained some terrorist activity in Malaya and Cyprus and increasing commitments in the Middle East and Persian Gulf areas. During the next ten years there was to be much troop redeployment as Britain withdrew from areas of the Commonwealth but entered into new regional defence alliances and military training agreements with emerging independent nations. Gradually the more distant overseas commitments reduced but not before a major conflict, euphemistically called 'confrontation', with Indonesia on the borders with Borneo and later a bitter anti-terrorist campaign in Aden.

Three major organisational changes in this decade were to affect the usage of military equipment. In 1963 the casting system was started. This, using terminology from the days of the military horse, involved the disposal of vehicles when their continued repair and maintenance became uneconomical and was applied on a basis of age or mileage to most common vehicles but initially not to specialist types. The economies were considerable since it was no longer necessary to hold spares for all types and models of vehicle until the last example was finally disposed of. In general all examples of a given batch were disposed of at about the same time. The other great saving was a reduction in the workshops required for the constant overhaul of old vehicles. The casting system quickly saw off most remaining wartime and early post-war vehicles but the cost of replacing specialist vehicles meant that no overnight replacement occurred of the older recovery tractors.

The second change was the end of conscription in 1963 and the establishment of a smaller all-Regular Army. This led to the disbandment of some units and was made feasible only by reduced overseas commitments. The other manpower resource available to replace the National Service conscript was the civilian. The Army had always employed civilians but in the 1960s the numbers were increased in static units. One result was that within the British Isles many REME recovery resources were entirely civilian manned though often by ex-REME tradesmen.

The next change was the disbandment of the Army Emergency Reserve (AER) and the Territorial Army and their replacement by a new and much smaller reserve organisation, the Territorial and Army Volunteer Reserve (T&AVR). The old TA had been organised as complete military divisions with all supporting troops. The new slimline reserve comprised only those units necessary to bring the Regular Army up to strength in wartime. A considerable reduction was made in REME units but those remaining included a number of recovery companies. The T&AVR required less equipment for training and gradually the stocks of vehicles held in depots for this purpose were run down. The intention was that the reserve component of the Army would no longer be a poor relation and would be provided with the same equipment as the Regular units. It would be some years before it was possible to achieve this with recovery vehicles.

The new technical phenomenon of the 1960s stemmed from a concept born in the 1950s. There was concern that in a war fuel stocks and distribution would become great problems and therefore all vehicles should be capable of running on any available fuel. It was found possible to adapt compression ignition (diesel) engines to run on most fuels and so the requirement was that all new vehicles should have diesel engines. The Chieftain tank, which was developed originally in the 1950s, was powered by the Leyland L60 vertically opposed piston diesel engine which had some basic design features in common with the wartime German Junkers Jumo aircraft engine. During the 1960s the Chieftain and a number of new diesel-engined trucks came into service. By this time the increased use of motor vehicles in Europe meant that petrol and diesel fuel stocks were at any time likely to be higher and the need for adaptable engines was lessened. The greater efficiency and economy of the diesel were to ensure its continued favour for more new Army vehicles after this time and over the next two decades the Meteor tank engine and Rolls B series petrol engines were gradually eclipsed.

Another decision to be put into operation during the 1960s was the wider employment of APCs. Prior to this they were operated mainly by the RAC and allocated to infantry units for specific operations or exercises. The 1-ton truck of the CT range built by Humber, had been tested with an armoured body in the late 1950s and proved to be a cheap and simple interim APC. It could carry a section of infantry or a support weapon and crew. Several hundred of these vehicles were built in the early 1960s, some of them on the chassis of the unarmoured trucks which were withdrawn from depot stocks for conversion.

Whilst these vehicles were being provided work was

progressing on the purpose-designed tracked APC, part of the FV 430 series. The basic APC variant, FV 432, was to have been named the Trojan but this was a commercial vehicle make at the time so the name was therefore dropped. Issues of the 432 began in the early 1960s and it is still in service. It was a box-shaped tracked carrier with a sloping glacis plate and vertical rear with a single door. The engine, mounted at the front on the left, drove the sprockets at the front of the track. The driver's position was on the right, beside the engine, and the vehicle commander sat to his rear. The APC weighed approximately 14 tons. Early versions were powered by the Rolls B Series 8-cylinder petrol engine but later types used a Rolls K60 multi-fuel diesel. Several variants of the basic APC were provided, in many cases differing only in stowage for each separate role but one more modified APC was a recovery vehicle developed from 1962, which came into service at the beginning of the 1970s. The recovery gear was provided as a 'kit' and consisted of a 6½-ton winch, later uprated to 8 tons, driven through a power take-off by the APC's main engine. At the rear were attachments for a folding spade anchor. As this prevented the rear door from opening the conversion involved shortening the door and fitting a blanking plate below it with an aperture for the winch rope. It was intended that the APC, fitted with the winch and anchor kit, should fill the recovery role in APC Infantry Battalions and those RA regiments equipped with the Abbot self-propelled gun. The recovery APC, never officially designated an ARV, was unpopular. Its winch was insufficiently powerful for major unditching tasks without laying out recovery tackle for a three to one pull. This was always a difficult and time-consuming operation and usually a heavy wheeled recovery vehicle or ARV could do the job with a straight pull, that is, within its winch's basic capacity.

In 1962 the Royal Horse Guards LAD met the need for recovery crew protection by converting, with War Office approval, a Ferret scout car to an ARV. The regiment was at the time in an airportable reconnaissance role but the contemporary airportable recovery vehicles were Land Rovers for which the 3½-ton Ferret was something of a handful. The ARV, based on a Ferret Mark 2 with its roof plate and turret removed, was fitted with a rear jib, towing hook, struts to block the rear suspension when towing and a Tirfor hand winch rigged to the jib. Other recovery gear was carried and a pedestal-mounted .30 inch Browning Machine Gun was fitted to give covering fire during recovery tasks. The vehicle was successfully tested and when the regiment changed roles the same vehicle with its turret refitted continued to undergo trials under REME Technical Group control. No further versions of this design were built except for a replica of the original in its later turreted form, which now stands outside the REME Museum.

During 1965 the 4th Royal Tank Regiment was deployed in Borneo, Sarawak and Brunei in a reconnaissance role. There, another recovery variant of the Ferret was used with a fixed jib attached to the engine decking and, again, using a portable winch. This seems to have been a much less elaborate conversion. It is not known whether it was designed by the regiment's LAD or by the Headquarters Far East Land Forces in Singapore.

Since the end of World War II Britain has depended for self-propelled medium and heavy artillery on American-designed and built equipment. When the M107 self-propelled 175mm gun was taken into use in the 1960s part of the package was the M578 ARV which used the same carriage as the gun. The main feature of this vehicle was a crane whose jib was raised and lowered hydraulically. The crane and its winch gear were housed in an armoured turret seated on the turret ring which would take the gun mounting on the M107 itself. The crane could lift over 12 tons yet the complete vehicle weighed only 22 tons. The

*The rear view of FV 432 with winch and anchor kit showing the congested interior and the shortened rear door.*

*The US M578 recovery variant of a basic chassis design common to several self-propelled guns.*

main winch could exert a 28-ton pull. One of the roles of the M578 was to carry out barrel changes for the guns. When the towed 8-inch howitzers used in some RA regiments were later converted to SP guns, using the same chassis as M107, the M578 became an appropriate ARV for these equipments also. This range of guns and the M578 have mainly been deployed in BAOR.

The Canadian Snomobile and its projected ARV variant were described in Chapter 3. When Britain later took on a NATO role of deploying forces in Norway for exercises and operations, various Swedish designed oversnow vehicles were adopted. The Volvo BV 202 articulated tracked vehicle was used from 1968 and later the Hagglunds BV 206. Winch-equipped versions of these vehicles were used by REME for recovery tasks. Neither of the Swedish-built vehicles was armoured. The BV202 proved a very useful vehicle in the boggy terrain of the Falkland Islands.

In 1961 Vickers began development of a commercial Medium or Main Battle Tank using the 105mm gun of the later Centurions but the automotive components of the Chieftain. The tank was in the 30-ton class then being advocated by some continental countries. Sales of the tank to India, Africa and the Middle East followed. In India the tank was locally manufactured as the Vijayanta in a factory at Avadi near the site of the REME Base Workshop of 1944/45. Later Vickers were to produce an ARV derivative of this tank. Although tested, these Vickers tanks were not operated by the British Army but RAC and REME personnel were involved in training projects in some countries which had purchased them.

As Leyland heavy recovery vehicles came into service in the 1960s the Army and REME were reducing in size. Despite this there was a need for large numbers of recovery vehicles to maintain war stocks and equip TA units for training. By then the diesel Scammells, a few of which were actually pre-war vehicles, were obsolete and hard pressed to cope not only with recovery loads but also modern tactical movement rates. Production of the 6×6 Scammell had ceased and therefore a new medium recovery vehicle was needed in order to complete the replacement of the old vehicles.

*Recovery using the winch equipped Volvo BV 202.*

*Recovery Vehicle Wheeled Medium AEC with additional cab
protection in Northern Ireland. A Saracen APC is on tow.*

AEC Ltd, then the renowned truck and bus manufacturer, had developed, during World War II, a 6-wheeled
version of the Matador which was mainly used as an RAF
aircraft refueller. Other experimental vehicles on this
chassis led to the Trucks and Tractors 10-ton GS 6×4 and
6×6 of the 1950s, some later examples of which remain in
service still. The next generation of heavy cargo vehicle was
based on the AEC Militant Mark 2, an updated version of
the 1950s series. A Militant based 6×6 tractor chassis
designated Militant Mark 3 was selected as a basis for the
new Recovery Vehicle Medium (FV 11044), design of
which began in 1964. Trials of prototypes took place
between 1967 and 1969. About 200 were eventually
purchased, coming into service from 1971.

The AEC used a similar hydraulic crane to that of the
Leyland. It could lift a maximum of 4½ tons. The chassis
was fitted with a mechanically driven 15-ton chassis winch.
The engine, an AEC AV 760 12.47-litre diesel, continued
the trend away from spark ignition engines for the heavier
vehicles. During trials of the new AEC, one failing which
caused problems was a tendency for the front of the vehicle
to lift when moving casualties on suspended tow up hills. In
order to cure this problem an ingenious cable operated
compensating gear or 'reactor' was fitted to hold down the
front end of the vehicle. This equipment was pioneered at
the Military Vehicle Engineering Establishment (MVEE)
and had the effect of safely increasing the weight that could
be suspended on the move; however, it was a time-
consuming chore to set up the equipment and this could
only be done after the casualty was suspended. In earlier
days a similar problem had been solved by steel counterweights on the front of the vehicle (Scammell 6×4 and
Austin 6×4 recovery vehicles) or even in some cases filling a
Scammell's front tyres with water instead of air! AECs came
into service in the 1970s, some, but not all, being fitted with
the reactor gear. Many of them remain in service today. No
major variants of the vehicle have been produced but those
used in Northern Ireland have been fitted with stone guards
(steel mesh) over windows and sometimes fibreglass armour
on the cab.

*The Berliet TBU 15 recovery vehicle being tested by REME.*

A different contender for the Scammell replacement
underwent trials in 1965 and 1966. In 1964 a collaborative
agreement was started between Alvis Ltd of Coventry and
the French firm Berliet. It was intended that the Stalwart
amphibian should be licence built for the French Army and
Berliet offered a 6×6 medium recovery vehicle for the
British Army. One appeared at the 1964 Commercial Motor
Show. Two TBU 15 CLD recovery vehicles were purchased
and tested, one in BAOR. Despite successful trials the
French vehicle was not adopted and the cooperation
agreement was terminated, possibly for fiscal or political
reasons. Another likely reason is the difficulty of having one
non-standard vehicle type in the Army with attendant
problems of spares supply. Once the AEC, now designated
Recovery Vehicle Wheeled, Medium, was deployed, many
Scammell Explorers became available to TA units. One or
two Pioneers even managed to soldier on in remote places,
the last in Belize where it was withdrawn from active use in
about 1980. It finally came back to Britain, to be restored
for the REME Museum collection.

In Berlin, the Mercedes 3-ton recovery vehicles and
Scammell Pioneers having become obsolete, two new heavy
recovery vehicles were purchased from Magirus Deutz in
West Germany. Based on the Uranus chassis they incorporated massive girder cranes which could carry out complete
lifts of vehicles involved in accidents. With the crane in the
travelling mode, jib forward, a smaller jib could be used for
suspended tows.

Shortly after World War II the US Army Ordnance
Department began the development of a series of standardised 2½-ton 6×6 and 5-ton 6×6 trucks to replace the
various makes in each class used in World War II. Each
range, although manufactured by different firms, was to a
common design and featured many standard components.
Within each range there was a recovery variant featuring the
type of pedestal-mounted hydraulic crane which was later to
be used on British vehicles. As the British Army adopted a
succession of US missile systems, initially Corporal then

*A Berlin Workshop special, the Magirus Deutz Uranus demonstrating its ability to lift a complete Scammell Explorer.*

*US Truck 5-ton 6×6 M246 combining a tractor for semi-trailer with recovery or workshop crane. These were used in RA missile regiments.*

Honest John and later Lance, a variety of US support vehicles came into British use including the 5-ton 6×6 wrecker M246. This was a long wheelbase variant of the standard 5-ton 6×6 chassis combining the function of tractor for semi-trailer, a fifth wheel coupling being fitted at the rear of the chassis, with that of recovery vehicle and crane. The usual Austin Western hydraulic crane was mounted midway along the chassis.

The Land Rover continued to provide the only recovery means for parachute units although much heavier vehicles could be carried in aircraft for air-mobile formations. In 1952 a number of Land Rovers were fitted with Turner winches at the front of the chassis, driven via a dog clutch from the crankshaft. It was intended to replace the original generation of 1-ton vehicles with multi-fuel diesel-engined vehicles but only a few of the Austin versions of these went into production. Experiments sought to achieve standardisation with the ¾-ton Land Rover to provide an airportable and amphibious 1-ton derivative but these attempts were inconclusive. One of these airportable 1-tonners was tested with a front-mounted Turner winch as a recovery vehicle in 1962/63.

An interesting conversion took place at 38 Central Workshop REME at some time in the early 1960s. This was the adaptation of a Scammell Pioneer gun tractor into a recovery vehicle. The tractor's steel body was retained, less the canopy and the recovery crane and counterweights transferred from a presumably worn out breakdown tractor.

When the War Office inherited the former MOS establishments, their domestic and some test vehicles came into the military vehicle orbit. Many were allocated Army numbers at this time, mostly in the series EP. They included a variety of recovery vehicles, some being wartime types. Among those 'series-converted' were a number of Bedford QL 3-tonners and AEC Matador tractors fitted with Harvey Frost recovery cranes. There is no indication that any of these, although technically military vehicles, were operated by the Army within its workshops or recovery units. Two recovery vehicles disposed of in 1974 bearing Army numbers which were probably from ex-MOS establishments were a Thornycroft Antar and a Scammell Constructor 20-ton tractor both fitted with recovery gear.

In the early 1960s the new Mark 3 version of the Thornycroft Antar began entering service. Given the FV number 12004, the new vehicle was designed for both the 50-ton and 60-ton semi-trailers and could be converted to a ballast-bodied tractor, FV 12006, for the Dyson 50-ton full trailer. These versions of the Antar were given a more streamlined appearance using a widened version of a cab utilised already on some Thornycroft commercial vehicles. Under the bonnet in place of the Meteorite petrol engine the Mark 3 used a Rolls 16.2-litre C8NFL diesel. The Mark 3 Antars remained in service with tank transporter squadrons of the Royal Corps of Transport (RCT) until the mid-1980s.

Associated Commercial Vehicles, the parent company of AEC, had taken over Thornycroft in 1960. Among many consequences of this venture was a one-off conversion of a Mark 2 Antar. This had the frame extended at the front and was fitted with an AEC 6-cylinder diesel engine normally used in the firm's dumper truck. This experimental vehicle, with its prominent extended bonnet, was taken into use by the Army after trials in 1963, finally being sold in 1971.

Other vehicles not primarily intended as transporters have been found very suitable at times. In the mid-1960s the Army was testing an AEC 10-ton truck fitted with a sliding tilt-bed body. This used a normal hydraulic tipping gear to elevate the body frame on which the body itself could slide to the rear until in contact with the ground. Small vehicles could then be winched onto the body and the process reversed to bring the vehicle body into a horizontal plane for transportation. Brimec equipment was used on this vehicle.

The virtues of the dummy axle have been described in Part 2, Chapter 3. This solution to the problem of recovering very heavy wheeled vehicles was financially more attractive than the provision of super-heavy recovery vehicles but, for a relatively simple equipment, it had a long gestation period. First thoughts of this solution to heavy vehicle recovery followed the cancellation of the super-heavy recovery vehicles in the 1950s. Design of Dummy Axle Recovery 10/30 ton (FV 3561) began in the early 1960s but although a prototype was under construction in 1962 it was not till 1971 that the equipment was accepted and production begun. The device was originally developed by Thornycrofts. It consisted of a single unsprung axle with two twin wheels and 10.00×15 tyres. The chassis carried a complex girder crane, the jib of which could be lowered and raised using a built-in powered hydraulic winch, thus lifting the front of the casualty. The raised vehicle was secured by an A frame. The production version of the Trailer Dummy Axle was fitted with mudguards and the power unit for the hydraulic system was changed to a diesel engine from the petrol engine of the prototype. Any heavy truck or tractor could tow this vehicle. With the demise of Thornycroft ROF Nottingham became involved with this device. Not long after the distribution of this Dummy Axle the use of the Eka recovery gear on heavy tractors largely made it obsolete.

*Dummy Axle 10/30-ton, a prototype on trials behind an AEC 6×6 tractor.*

# Chapter 5
# The 1970s and 1980s: Newer Armoured Recovery Vehicles

These decades were characterised for the Army by a more continuous quest for economies. One major problem had been that to attract sufficient men into an all-Regular army in the 1960s, a time of full employment and affluence, Army pay had to be increased. It had in consequence become the biggest single element of the annual budget and could only be reduced by having fewer soldiers. As the 1970s continued with considerable retrenchment in industry and increasing unemployment and thus at last a ready supply of manpower for the Armed Forces, there was paradoxically great pressure to limit or reduce military strengths in order to provide sufficient funds for new equipment.

Several ways for the Army to afford new equipment were adopted. Firstly quantities, once justified, were sometimes purchased over an extended period making the re-equipment process long drawn out and giving a longer period with old and new types remaining in service side by side. In consequence spare parts holdings and training in the repair of the old design had to continue. The extended service of older equipment often produced a disproportion-ate repair workload. A second way of saving on new equipment, not applicable to weapon systems, was to take as far as possible off-the-shelf commercial vehicles. Another device was the promotion of overseas sales of British military equipment which helped to defray development costs. Collaborative projects with other NATO countries served the same purpose.

Many new items of equipment came into service during the 1970s and development continued, but for wheeled vehicles there began a gradual change to greater reliance on the manufacturers for the initiation of designs, thus allowing the FVRDE (MVEE from 1970) to concentrate more on armoured and specialist vehicle design and the testing of prototypes. The increasing complexity of military equipment coincided with increasing demands for financial savings, two largely incompatible requirements. At the same time far greater emphasis was placed during the design stage on reliability. In 1972 wheeled recovery vehicles were brought into the casting system with a designated lifetime of seventeen years. This partly reflected the fact that they spent more time than cargo vehicles stationary, awaiting an emergency, and also took account of the high cost of replacements.

During the 1970s a review of future requirements for B

vehicles followed the adoption in 1969 of metric units: thus the new fleet was to be in 1-tonne, 4-tonne, 8-tonne, 16-tonne and 20-tonne load capacities. The CT, GS and CL vehicle concept was superseded by GS and CL vehicles in two categories, Low Mobility and Medium Mobility. The former were essentially modified civilian vehicles while the latter in most cases featured all-wheel-drive. The sole High Mobility Load Carrier in service was the Alvis Stalwart.

The successor to the Centurion tank, the Chieftain, FV 4201, was designed in the 1950s. By 1959 an ARV had been included in the range of vehicles using the Chieftain hull but for a time it was decided not to proceed with the design as the Centurion ARV Mark 2 was just coming into service and was quite adequate for the job. In 1964 the new Ministry of Defence (Army), successors to the War Office, produced a General Staff Operational Requirement for a Chieftain ARV in order to benefit from the commonality of design and spares. Design began at the ROF at Leeds in conjunction with FVRDE which allocated the FV number 4204. Two pilot models were later built, becoming available for trials in 1971. The design, for the first time in a British ARV, provided for winching from the front of the vehicle, its spade anchor doubling as a dozer blade. This layout had been favoured in earlier US and continental designed ARVs. It had the advantage that the crew were facing the casualty which simplified control. The Chieftain's 30-ton main winch was mechanically driven and was of the double capstan type. In this the strain is taken by a small capstan with one layer of winch rope on it. Behind it the bulk of the rope is stored on an unstressed drum geared to the capstan. This prevents crushing of the rope under the strain of winching. In addition to this main winch a smaller 3½-ton capacity hydraulically driven winch was incorporated which could be used to draw out the heavy main winch rope, relieving the recovery mechanics of a time-consuming, arduous task. This auxiliary winch could also be used for minor recovery jobs. The commander's cupola in the new ARV was designed to give a good all-round view when closed down and incorporated night viewing devices. In practice the clutter of winch rope guides and other necessary paraphernalia on the vehicle's roof somewhat limited the view. Trials of the new ARV took place at FVRDE and at SEME over a period of about two years and after some design changes the vehicle was accepted into service in 1973. Production followed, vehicles being based on the Chieftain Mark 5 hull and by 1979 nearly 40 ARVs had been issued.

The Chieftain's engine weighed about 4½ tons, much more than the Centurion's Meteor. The crane on the Carrier Maintenance, FV 434, was strengthened to cope with this but there loomed on the horizon a new tank in which, for the first time, the engine and gearbox-cum-steering unit would be changed as a complete assembly or power pack weighing about 6 tons. The new tank was developed originally for Iran and was named the Shir Iran. After the revolution a much improved version of the Shir was adopted by the British Army as the Challenger, reviving a name used during World War II for a lengthened Cromwell with a

*Chieftain Armoured Repair and Recovery Vehicle with the 6-tonne crane jib raised and showing the cradle for carrying a spare engine.*

17-pounder gun. Iran had purchased Chieftain tanks from Britain and the associated ARVs were modified to cope with engine changes of the projected Shir by fitting them with a crane. To cope with Challenger it was decided to similarly modify British Army Chieftain ARVs. The altered vehicles were designated Armoured Repair and Recovery Vehicles (ARRVs). They were fitted with Atlas AK6000 hydraulic cranes on the left side of the rear of the hull and with cradles over the engine compartment which were designed to carry spare power packs. Vickers produced conversion kits and the modifications were made in 38 Central Workshop REME in UK and in 23 Base Workshop REME in Germany. While Chieftain ARVs were withdrawn for modification, units were issued with Centurion Mark 2 ARVs which had previously been withdrawn from service. These proved still to be very effective and some remain in use some thirty years after they were originally designed.

The new Challenger tank pioneered the use of composite armour developed at the Royal Armament Research and Developing Establishment (RARDE) and known as Chobham armour. The vehicle was powered by a conventional V 12-cylinder diesel engine of Rolls Royce design which proved to be very reliable. The tank's suspension system was new but the best feature of the Chieftain, its gun, was incorporated into Challenger.

This time the ARV development was more in step with the parent tank and a Challenger ARRV was called for promptly, development by Vickers Defence Systems beginning early in the 1980s. In August 1987 the first of six pre-production ARRVs was completed. Two were soon available for REME trials. The new vehicle's mechanical components were common to the gun tank. Its recovery

*A prototype of the Challenger ARRV.*

equipment consisted of a Rotzler Treibmatic capstan winch, hydraulically driven and with a 50-tonne direct pull. An auxiliary winch was fitted and also an Atlas AK 6000 M8 hydraulic crane. The front mounted dozer blade, forward winching layout and rear-mounted crane all served to give this ARRV a superficial resemblance to its predecessor, but it was in fact a much more powerful vehicle with many more sophisticated features under the skin.

While the Challenger ARRV was under development for the British Army, Vickers Defence Systems were applying an entirely new concept to the ARV. This involved a simple conversion of any gun tank by fitting it with an ARV turret which contained a winch and was fitted with a lifting boom for repair tasks. This conversion kit was aimed at commercial sales. A model showed the turret based on a US M48 tank chassis.

The British Army nearly had yet another ARV when development of the self-propelled version of the FH 70 howitzer was progressing. This equipment was a joint project with Germany and Italy and in 1978 it was suggested that there should be an ARV version, but instead the requirement for later ARVs included an ability to recover the SP 70. This became unnecessary when the joint venture was abandoned.

In 1964 FVRDE began development of a new range of tracked light reconnaissance vehicles to replace the Alvis FV 600 range of wheeled vehicles, Saladin and Saracen. Alvis were awarded the contract for production of the new series in 1967. The basic vehicle was, officially, a Combat Vehicle Reconnaissance (Tracked), CVR(T), but was in practical terms a light tank. The Scorpion (FV 101) was armed with a 76mm gun while the similar Scimitar (FV 107) carried a 30mm single shot or burst fire Rarden gun.

The series used aluminium armour which had been pioneered in the USA with, in particular, the M113 APC. The power unit, mounted at the front of the hull beside the driver, was a Jaguar 4.2-litre petrol engine. The vehicles were all very compact and weighed in the region of 7 tons. The small size made the vehicles somewhat cramped, the Spartan APC being able to carry only four men in addition to its crew. The diminutive size and high speed were considered important assets in the reconnaissance role. The many variants of the FV 100 series included an ARV which was developed from 1970 and named Sampson (FV 106). This was based on the Spartan APC hull but fitted with a 3-ton capstan winch. In order to carry out most recovery tasks it was necessary to lay out reduction tackle and an extra-long winch rope was provided for this purpose. One result of this was once again a very cramped interior. The two separate rear spades, required to preserve access to the vehicle's rear door, were provided with a detachable bridging blade. The light weight of the vehicle frequently resulted in the front end lifting when winching. A tubular steel jib kit was carried and could be fitted to the vehicle's roof and held in place by wire stays when in use. An array of recovery tools and stores were stowed in and on this very small vehicle. One of its distinctions was that Sampson was the newest REME ARV to see war service, one being used during the Falklands war. During the campaign it fell into a drainage ditch and was unceremoniously hoisted out by the surviving Chinook helicopter. Although stemming from a 1960s series design, Sampson did not enter service until the early 1980s.

During the 1960s and early 1970s US experience in Vietnam began to reflect the long-held German view that the APC should be a fighting vehicle rather than an armoured transport vehicle. There followed in most countries a new generation of Infantry Combat Vehicles with larger turret-mounted guns in place of the earlier machine-guns and apertures for the on-board infantry section to fire its weapons from inside the vehicle. After a long period of studies and development starting in the late 1960s, Britain's contender, the Warrior (FV 500 series), was unveiled by its builder, GKN Sankey, in 1980. Some 10 tons heavier than the FV 432, one version of the new vehicle carried a Rarden gun and a machine-gun in its turret.

Early in its development thought was given to the REME support vehicles. Two were proposed, an ARRV which would have a 20-tonne winch and a 6-tonne hydraulic crane and also a forward repair vehicle, for the same role as the FV 434, which would have only the crane. Development of these vehicles continues.

The Humber 'Pigs' used in Northern Ireland were already long in the tooth when in the early 1970s GKN began to develop a wheeled armoured carrier for a similar role. Eventually a version of this private venture was selected by MOD(A) to equip mechanised infantry battalions for those tasks not involving the direct support of tanks, for which the Warrior was intended. The new wheeled APC, named Saxon, was brought into service in the early 1980s and among its derivatives was a wheeled ARV with an externally mounted winch.

*Sampson light ARV of the CVR series shown at Port Stanley in the Falklands. The bridging piece which joins the two spade anchors can be seen on the side of the vehicle.*

# Chapter 6
# Further Progress in Wheeled Recovery Vehicles and Transporters

The multi-fuel engine concept of the late 1950s coincided with a need for a replacement of the basic truck 3-ton GS range of vehicles produced in the early and mid-1950s. After competitive trials in the mid-1960s, a Bedford Model MK was selected in 1968 and began to enter service soon after, classed as a 4-ton truck. In 1977 the specialist vehicle and body builders Reynolds Boughton were advertising a commercial recovery vehicle with an hydraulic crane and based on the new Bedford MK chassis. At about this time the Army decided to replace the Bedford RL light recovery

vehicle and carried out trials of two Bedford Boughtons in 1980. The single rear wheels of the commercial prototype were replaced with twin rear wheels, as had featured on the earlier Bedford. At one stage during the trials there were thoughts of basing the vehicle on the larger Bedford 8-tonne TM4-4 chassis but the modified MK chassis was eventually accepted and put into production as the Bedford MJ. The vehicle was fitted with a 6-tonne main winch. It began to enter service in 1981.

At some time in the later 1960s or 1970s a most unusual

*The commercial prototype Bedford Boughton Light Recovery Vehicle which was developed into the Bedford MJ.*

Land Rover was produced for use in amphibious trials at Instow. This was fitted with a winch and built in flotation panels. It is not known if this vehicle was intended as a beach recovery vehicle.

Towards the end of the 1960s, a vehicle was urgently needed as a tractor for the new 105mm light gun. The Rover company had earlier built a 1¼-ton forward control vehicle for commercial use, adopted by the Army as a fire tender. A lighter, wider development followed with, for the first time, its load capacity rated in metric units. It used many Range Rover components and was pitted for trials in 1971 against a Volvo truck based on the Laplander forward-control vehicle used by the Swedish Army. The truck 1-tonne 4×4 Rover was selected for production in 1973. Besides its gun tractor role, some were allocated to REME units in support of airborne and airportable formations and workshops began their own experiments to produce special versions, the recovery vehicle having a fold-away jib. This enabled it to carry cargo when not required for recovery tasks.

There have been occasions in some operational areas when, for security reasons, REME have operated civilian pattern recovery vehicles to tow away other vehicles whose military connections could not be advertised. Keeping to its

special arrangements for obtaining new equipment, Berlin Brigade acquired four Volvo F88 4×4 recovery tractors fitted with Eka recovery gear. These were used among other things for recovering brokendown military and allied civilian vehicles on the autobahn between Berlin and West Germany. Local provisioning was also extended to Canada

*Truck 1-tonne 4×4 Rover with folding recovery jib.*

*A special Landrover with winch and flotation panels used at the former Fording Trials Branch REME.*

where the REME workshop at the Suffield training area was equipped with a number of Canadian-built Western Star 5-ton 6×6 recovery vehicles. These are basically commercial types with Holmes twin-boom wrecker gear (see Part 3) and were produced to a specification drawn up in Canada. One of these vehicles has been photographed in colour and is shown to be painted red, presumably so as to make it clearly visible on the plain when carrying out non-tactical recovery tasks in danger areas.

In 1972 there were still 330 Scammell Explorers and Pioneers in service, though few of the latter. Despite the earlier influx of Leylands and newly arriving AECs, there was still a need to replace these aged Scammells. At this time the country was in the throes of a financial crisis and MOD budgets were hard hit. The AEC had been somewhat less successful than hoped and the take over of the company by Leyland in 1962 had led by the 1970s to much rationalisation of products so there was soon no chance of obtaining more AECs. The cost of specially developed recovery vehicles, which were rarely cheap enough for

*One of the Berlin Volvo F88 4×4 recovery vehicles with Eka equipment.*

*The Canadian Western Star 6×6 recovery vehicle with Holmes Wrecker Gear.*

commercial sales, had to be borne entirely by the armed services, so during the 1970s the MOD began to look more closely at what commercial firms were producing and using for recovery. True, many were using ex-WD vehicles with which generations of REME recovery mechanics would have been familiar, but some new concepts were appearing, based on the increasing use of hydraulic cranes and recovery gear.

The Eka company of Stockholm, Sweden, had designed a new type of recovery vehicle in which not only were all movements of lifting gear and the main winch itself actuated by hydraulics but also the two rear spades or anchors. Another unusual feature was that the whole installation, including the main winch, formed part of the recovery body, thus simplifying its fitting to a variety of chassis. The basic component was a cranked jib, raised by hydraulic rams so as to lift casualties for suspended tows in contrast to the more common system of a fixed jib and a winch to raise the casualty. A variety of fitments could be attached to the end of the Eka jib to suit attachment points at the front or rear of any vehicle casualty. The main winch cable could be used for recovery or, over the jib in its raised position, as a crane hoist. The jib when raised in the suspended tow mode was locked into position by steel pins. The main disadvantage in the crane role was the lack of slewing movement. Maximum lift on the move was in the region of 15 tonnes depending on the chassis to which the equipment was fitted.

In 1970 an Eka crane on a 6×4 Volvo chassis was purchased for trials. After it had been tested in, among other places, Northern Ireland, it was decided in 1972 to purchase the bodies only for fitting to the 6×4 Scammell Crusader chassis, then coming into use as a tractor for equipment carrying semi-trailers (see page 95). The Scammell Eka lacked drive to the front wheels and was therefore classed as a civilian or low-mobility vehicle, due to its restricted cross-country performance, but its recovery gear made it suitable for the peace-time recovery organisation and adequate for a route-clearance role in war. Its arrival not only sped some of the older petrol engined Scammells on their way to retirement but, after the AEC and Leyland, it revived the name of the firm which had for so many years been synonymous with military recovery vehicles. The new vehicle was fitted with a 20-tonne main winch and front mounted 7-tonne self-recovery winch. The maximum lift for suspended tows was originally listed as seven and a half tons but in service far greater loads were moved. A prototype Scammell Crusader Eka was demonstrated at the 1976 Commercial Motor Show and 130 vehicles were ordered in 1977. These were completed and deployed to units by mid-1980.

As the 1970s progressed, the Leyland heavy recovery vehicle became obsolescent. Its petrol engine was both uneconmical and no longer powerful enough for present needs. The AEC was also to become a problem as a product of a now defunct company. Following the adoption of the Scammell Crusader Eka Low Mobility Recovery Vehicle, the solution to a Leyland and AEC replacement seemed to

*A tour de force. A Scammell Crusader Eka towing, suspended, an Antar which had burnt out. The 60-ton semi-trailer carries a prototype SP 70 self-propelled howitzer. The Scammell is lifting 15–20 tons and towing about 90 tons.*

lie in the excellent Eka gear allied to a modern 6×6 chassis.

Fodens of Sandbach in Cheshire were an old-established firm which pioneered steam lorries in the nineteenth century. During World War II they had supplied 10-ton 6×4 and 6-ton 4×2 chassis to the Army but not till the 1970s were they once again to supply military vehicles. The first new Fodens were basically civilian pattern 8-wheeled 8×4 types of 20-tonne cargo and fuel carriers, but eventually a 6×6 vehicle was developed mainly as a tractor for the new 155mm FH70 field gun. The company had been taken over by the US Paccar company at about this time but continued to market its vehicles under the Foden name. The gun tractor chassis was adapted to take the Eka body and six vehicles were purchased for trials. It had long been a REME requirement that a wheeled recovery vehicle should be multipurpose and capable of use as a crane. The lack of a slewing crane on the Scammell Eka had been accepted due to its restricted role and the speed of introduction of a commercial equipment.

Production versions of the Foden Eka were to use an adaptation of the original recovery body featuring a more conventional Atlas-designed pedestal-mounted hydraulic crane. This, however, was mounted above the cranked recovery jib. The latter was lifted now by the crane's winch rope instead of its own hydraulic rams. Once the casualty had been raised the recovery jib was locked into position as in the original design: thus the equipment retained the best features of the basic design plus a crane. The vehicle was powered by a Rolls (now Perkins) Eagle diesel engine. The Rotzler-designed main winch was rated at 25-tonnes and the Turner front winch at 10 tonnes. Maximum lift of the crane with the vehicle stationary was 12 tonnes and the maximum

*The Foden Eka Medium Mobility Recovery Vehicle towing a laden Taskers 20-tonne trailer. The load is an AEC 10-ton truck fitted with HIAB crane.*

suspended load, when moving, 11 tonnes. The tyres were 16.00×20. Two side-mounted hydraulically-extended stabilisers, together with the rear spade anchor, provided a solid base for crane work.

By 1986 and after extensive trials the first of 333 Foden Medium Mobility Recovery Vehicles were beginning to enter service. They then began to replace the surviving Scammell Explorers and Leylands.

Scammell had for many years been a Leyland subsidiary and after the take over of AEC, Leyland concentrated all heavy and specialist vehicle development at Watford. Following the highly successful Constructor, Scammell produced a new 6×4 heavy haulage tractor with a streamlined bonnet shape under which various engine options were offered. This was the Scammell Contractor. When it too ceased production two new heavy Scammells were designed both using standard Leyland cabs. The S24, normal control, and S26, forward control, heavy tractors were produced in 6×4 and 6×6 versions.

While Britain had declined to supply weapons to Iran and Iraq after the start of the Gulf war, Iraq had previously purchased some logistic vehicles including a somewhat unusual recovery vehicle. This was based on a 6×6 derivative of the Scammell Contractor and was called a Contractor Explorer, thus reviving the name of the earlier recovery tractor. Reynolds Boughton recovery gear was fitted and one example of the vehicle was tested by REME. Similar equipment was fitted to a demonstration model of the Scammell S24 in 1981 when the MOD was considering the Foden prototypes. As a result, Scammell offered an equivalent vehicle for comparative trials. This was an S26 with the prototype of the Eka recovery body used later on the production Fodens. The Scammell was tested at MVEE and at SEME but, although quite highly rated, the Foden was selected for production.

By the late 1960s it was clear that a replacement for the Thornycroft Antars would be needed since they were no longer built and spares would eventually be scarce. Added to this, the firm had been absorbed by AEC, which itself subsequently disappeared into the Leyland conglomerate. Another problem was that the design was still basically that of the mid-1940s and a transporter was needed that would reflect some of the progress in automotive engineering design. In response to a 1969 FVRDE specification Scammell produced prototypes of their Commander tractor and a matching 65-tonne semi-trailer was designed and built by Crane Fruehauf. The vehicle was given extensive trials before being adopted by the Army and coming into service in early 1984. About 130 were purchased for use by RCT tank transporter units.

The Scammell Commander equalled the Antar in size but was a more powerful vehicle with a Rolls Royce designed CV12TCE turbo-charged diesel engine. An Allison epicyclic gearbox transmitted power to the rear axles. Although primarily a road transporter, the vehicle's reserve of power enabled it to operate off roads on firm ground. A German Rotzler two-speed winch was fitted after early prototypes had used a Turner winch. As most Commanders would be deployed in BAOR the tractors were built with left-hand drive.

The RE plant transport situation remained largely unchanged throughout the 1960s except that some additional Scammell Constructors were received and these, in some cases, were fitted with fixed mudguards in place of the cycle type used on earlier vehicles. Towards the end of the decade a newer tractor was sought and a roadgoing 6×4 tractor, the forward control Scammell Crusader, was selected. As tractor 20-tonne it was to be used by the RCT with a high-platform cargo semi-trailer (FV 3242). These came into use in the early 1970s. The RE versions, tractor 35-tonne, were ordered in 1977 together with a new Crane Fruehauf 35-tonne low-bed semi-trailer. The 35-tonne Crusader was fitted with a Plumett winch and carried a

*The Scammell Commander 65 tonne tank transporter.*

*The Scammell S26 alternative offered in competition with the Foden Eka recovery vehicle.*

*The Scammell Crusader with a drop-frame semi-trailer with detachable swan neck.*

sleeper cab. The power unit was a Rolls Eagle diesel. Some early versions of the Crusader were tested with different trailers and some are believed to have been used with the semi-trailer from the Scammell Constructor. The new Crane Fruehauf semi-trailer dispensed with the full-width ramp and reverted to the more usual twin ramps. The purpose remained the carriage of both wheeled and tracked RE plant, including the multi-purpose armoured Combat Engineer Tractor. Subsequently Army Crusaders have been used with other semi-trailers including a Craven Tasker 37-tonne low bed trailer with three axles and a drop-frame 2-axle trailer with detachable swan neck. Some Crusader tractors with semi-trailers have been issued to REME units and all versions have carried armoured vehicles within their load capacity.

Throughout the 1970s and 1980s various commercial heavy tractors and tank transporters were tested at Chertsey using, in some cases, standard British Army semi-trailers and in others, commercial trailers. Versions of the Scammell Constructor, Contractor, S24 and S26 were tried using the excellent facilities at MVEE, (later RARDE). Another 6×6 Scammell S26, on six single-tyred wheels and with a platform body, was tested carrying a FV 432. Somewhat earlier, two Foden 6×4 heavy tractors were purchased for trials with 50-ton semi-trailers.

The Army continued to need small recovery trailers for lighter loads, including disabled B vehicles. Increasingly it was decided to seek commercial trailers if this could save development costs without prejudicing the suitability of the equipment for its role. In the mid-1970s a tilt-bed platform trailer was tested. In this the main chassis was fitted with two close-coupled axles at the centre, each with two twin wheels. When the platform was tilted to the rear two small ramps enabled a casualty to be winched on board using the trailer's 4-tonne hand-winch. Rated at 10 tonnes, these trailers were purchased starting in 1978 with 88 earmarked for REME. Several, generally similar, types were built by Crane Fruehauf, Multiwheeler, Weekes and other manufacturers.

For small vehicles, such as Landrovers (the one word trade mark was adopted in recent years) and staff cars, various commercial trailers have been tried and some purchased. Some types had two close-coupled wheels on each side, similar to some horse-box trailers, and platforms which could be lowered to the ground; others had fixed floors and folding ramps. Various makes used included Eezion, Courtburn Lolode and Harvey Frost. A much larger recovery trailer, taken into use in 1978, was the Craven Tasker 20-tonne 3-axle trailer. This was fitted with turntable steering and two hinged ramps. It could carry wheeled or light tracked vehicles.

During the development of the Dummy Axle 10/30 ton (see Chapter 4), the idea was seen as a means of providing a cheap recovery equipment for units whose vehicle usage did not warrant the provision of a recovery vehicle which might spend much time standing idle. A smaller, Dummy Axle 1/5 ton (FV 2691), later rated in metric units, was designed

*A 10-tonne tilt bed recovery trailer.*

for this role and development began in the late 1960s. Once again this proved a long process. Two completely different designs evolved, one version having a fixed jib and twin wheels on the axle and another being a smaller version of the 10/30-tonne trailer with single wheels but an unpowered winch to raise the jib. There were many delays in trials so that deployment of production trailers did not take place till the early 1980s. The production version built by Rubery Owen used the fixed jib. It could lift 3 tonnes, enabling it to recover any of the 4-tonne capacity trucks in common use.

An extension of the tilting and sliding body idea demonstrated on the AEC Brimec 10-tonner was used for commercial purposes and steadily refined over the years. In this the whole body could be dismounted and the base vehicle driven away to collect another. This evolved into the military Demountable Rack Offloading and Pick Up System (DROPS), which was pioneered by Reynolds Boughton. Although primarily intended as ammunition carriers, various prototype DROPS vehicles have been tested carrying armoured vehicles.

Another dismountable body transporter was built by Terex using the 2-wheeled tractor part of an earthmoving machine with a demountable platform body on the rear section. This was photographed in 1985 carrying a FV 432 APC and whilst bearing a British Army number was in fact an export vehicle.

This survey of British Army recovery vehicles, whilst extensive, cannot claim completeness since so many experimental or locally improvised types have not been widely publicised. It does, however, give the reader a fairly comprehensive coverage of those types of vehicle used or tested in the recovery or transporter roles. It illustrates the constant quest for new and improved means of salvaging damaged Army vehicles quickly, efficiently and with as much ease as can be derived from the advances in technology. Whatever path future recovery vehicle development may take there is little doubt that it will lead to further improvements as newer materials and manufacturing techniques appear. Inevitably such vehicles will be more complex in design but hopefully even more simple to operate. They will, by their specialist nature, continue to interest and intrigue the armchair students of military equipment.

# Glossary of Abbreviations

| | |
|---|---|
| AA | Anti-Aircraft |
| ADGB | Air Defence of Great Britain |
| AEC | Associated Equipment Company |
| AER | Army Emergency Reserve |
| AFV | Armoured Fighting Vehicle |
| ALFSEA | Allied Land Forces South East Asia |
| AOC | Army Ordnance Corps |
| AOD | Army Ordnance Department |
| APC | Armoured Personnel Carrier |
| ARV | Armoured Recovery Vehicle |
| ARRV | Armoured Repair and Recovery Vehicle |
| ASC | Army Service Corps |
| | |
| BAOR | British Army of the Rhine |
| BARV | Beach Armoured Recovery Vehicle |
| BEF | British Expeditionary Force |
| bhp | brake horse power |
| BLA | British Liberation Army |
| BMC | British Motor Corporation |
| | |
| CKD | Completely Knocked Down |
| CL | Civilian |
| CMP | Canadian Military Pattern |
| COXE | Combined Operations Experimental Establishment |
| CT | Combat |
| cwt | hundredweight (1/20th of an Imperial ton) |
| CVR(T) | Combat Vehicle Reconnaissance (Tracked) |
| DD | Duplex Drive |
| DME | Director of Mechanical Engineering |
| DOS(E) | Director of Ordnance Services (Engineering) |
| DTD&E | Department of Tank Design and Experiment |
| | |
| EBRS | Experimental Beach Recovery Section |
| ERS | Experimental Recovery Section |
| EXBX | Model designation of Mack truck |
| | |
| FMR | Fitter Motor Transport (Recovery) |
| FVDE | Fighting Vehicle Design Establishment |
| FVPE | Fighting Vehicle Proving Establishment |
| FVRDE | Fighting Vehicle Research and Development Establishment |
| | |
| GS | General Service |
| | |
| HMLC | High Mobility Load Carrier |
| hp | horse power |
| | |
| IAOC | Indian Army Ordnance Corps |
| IEME | Indian Electrical and Mechanical Engineers |
| | |
| LAD | Light Aid Detachment |
| LMSW | Model designation of a Mack track |
| LofC | Lines of Communication |
| LVT | Landing Vehicle Tracked |

| | |
|---|---|
| MDAP | Marshall Defence Aid Plan |
| MEE | Mechanisation Experimental Establishment |
| MGC | Machine Gun Corps |
| MGO | Master General of Ordnance |
| MOS | Ministry of Supply |
| mph | miles per hour |
| MT | Mechanical Transport (also Motor Transport) |
| MTDE | Maintenance Techniques Development Establishment |
| MVEE | Military Vehicle Engineering Establishment |
| MWEE | Mechanical Warfare Experimental Establishment |
| | |
| NATO | North Atlantic Treaty Organisation |
| NLE | Naval Land Equipment |
| | |
| PAIFORCE | Persia and Iraq Force |
| POW | Prisoner of War |
| | |
| QMG | Quarter Master General |
| | |
| RA | Royal Artillery |
| RAC | Royal Armoured Corps |
| RAEME | Royal Australian Electrical and Mechanical Engineers |
| RAF | Royal Air Force |
| RAOC(E) | Royal Army Ordnance Corps (Engineering Branch) |
| RARDE | Royal Armament Research and Development Establishment |
| RASC | Royal Army Service Corps |
| RCOC | Royal Canadian Ordnance Corps |
| RCT | Royal Corps of Transport |
| RE | Royal Engineers |
| REME | Royal Electrical and Mechanical Engineers |
| RFC | Royal Flying Corps |
| RIASC | Royal Indian Army Service Corps |
| RNAS | Royal Naval Air Service |
| RNZEME | Royal New Zealand Electrical and Mechanical Engineers |
| ROF | Royal Ordnance Factory |
| ROK | Republic of Korea |
| RTC | Royal Tank Corps |
| RTR | Royal Tank Regiment |
| | |
| SEAC | South East Asia Command |
| | |
| TA | Territorial Army |
| T&AVR | Territorial and Army Volunteer Reserve |
| | |
| UK | United Kingdom |
| US | United States |
| USAAF | United States Army Air Force |
| | |
| WD | War Department |
| WVEE | Wheeled Vehicle Experimental Establishment |

# Acknowledgements

Inevitably a book of this sort includes material from the recollections, researches and the photograph and data collections of many individuals. It is made possible by the access given to records and the assistance of the staff in many organisations besides the REME Museum. I am indebted to:

the Imperial War Museum, the Tank Museum, the Museum of Army Transport, the RCT Museum, the RAOC Museum, the School of Electrical and Mechanical Engineering REME, Vickers Defence Systems, the REME Journal, Craftsman Magazine and MB Transport Photographs.

I wish to thank the following, among them some friends of many years standing, who have contributed information and photographs either to the REME Museum, to my collection or specifically for this book:

Lt Col RJ Alexander, Mr Clem Atlee, Col JCM Baker, Mr G Bradnam, Mr J Church, Mr M Conniford, Mr DJ Davies, Mr RA Dixon, Lt Col WJ Exley, Mr D Fletcher, Mr L Freathy, Mr P Gaine, Mr BS Gilbert, Mr P Hancox, Maj P Handel, Mr J Harrington, Maj M Hay, Ssgt R Jones, Mr H Kemp, Mr J MacDonald, Col PR MacIver, Mr J McLaughlin, Lt Col WF Nesbitt, Mr T O'Callaghan, Mr K Pavitt, Mr R Pattison, Mr R Peskett, Brig CIE Rabagliati, Mr AM Reedman, Mr D Spicer, Mr LA Staines, Mr RA Stevens, Mr N Tarling, Col PR Tozer, Mr BH Vanderveen, Lt Col PWH Whiteley OBE, Maj B Woods.

To any readers who feel that they too should be listed on this page I apologise since so much information has come to me over the years and not all sources have been recorded at the time.

In addition I must thank David Ross who has produced copies of borrowed photos for me at times for a number of years, Col DA Morrison and Col IG Swan both of whom encouraged me to turn the REME Journal articles into a book, my daughter Mrs Teresa McCurrach and Mrs Eileen Butterworth who jointly turned my hieroglyphics into typescript and finally my wife Jane who has endured long silences, mountains of paper, references and photos as each room of the house became a branch of the office.

# Index

A20 (tank)  26, 50
A41 (tank)  51, 76
A45 (tank)  76, 77
A46 (tank)  78
A vehicle  10, 12, 15, 39, 64, 65, 77
Ackerman (steering gear)  34, 50
AEC  3, 16, 18, 19, 20, 25, 28, 29, 35, 36, 37, 72, 79, 84, 85, 86, 93, 94, 95, 96
Afrika Korps  38, 39
Airborne Force Development Centre  42
Air defence of Great Britain (ADGB)  13
Alam Halfa  39
Albion  15, 33, 37, 44, 52, 59, 67, 73
Aldershot  12, 14, 20, 46, 49, 75
Allied Land Forces South East Asia (ALFSEA)  59
Allison  95
Alvis  84, 87, 89
Amesbury  42
Antar (Mighty Antar) (tractor)  71, 72, 73, 85, 94, 95
Anti-Aircraft (AA)  13, 42, 47
Antwerp  55
Anzio  46
Appledore  53
Arakan  59
Arborfield  41, 47, 48, 49, 52, 56
Ardennes  24, 55
armoured car  4, 8, 12, 17, 78, 79
armoured personnel carrier (APC)  78, 81, 89, 96
armoured recovery vehicle (ARV)  8, 22, 36, 37, 40, 42, 43, 46, 47, 48, 49, 52, 53, 57, 61, 72, 74, 75, 76, 77, 78, 79, 80, 82, 83, 87, 88, 89, 90
armoured repair and recovery vehicle (ARRV)  88, 89
Armoured Replacement Group  37
Armstrong Siddeley  12
Army Emergency Reserve (AER)  81
Army Estimates  12
Army Ordnance Corps (AOC) (Soldiers)  4, 5
Army Ordnance Department (AOD) (Officers)  2, 5
Army Service Corps (ASC)  2, 3, 4, 6
army tank brigade  24, 25, 40, 57
Arnhem  55
Arras  24
Ashanti War  2
Assam  59
Atherton Turret Hoist  80
Atlantic (Tractor)  72
Atlas (Crane)  88, 89, 94

Austin  42, 56, 65, 68, 70, 84, 85
Austin Western (Crane)  69, 85
Auxiliary Fire Service  68
Avadi  83

B40 (Engine)  65
B60 (Engine)  65
B80 (Engine)  65
B81 (Engine)  68, 76
B Vehicles  10, 12, 13, 27, 51, 64, 65, 72, 87, 96
BV 202 (Snow vehicle)  83
BV 206 (Snow vehicle)  83
backloading  vi, 37, 55, 80
BARBAROSSA  38
Bari  43
Basingstoke  71
Bauly  19
beach armoured recovery vehicle (BARV)  53, 54, 77, 79, 80
Beda Fomm  38
Bedford  42, 52, 56, 68, 69, 73, 75, 85, 91
Benghazi  38
Berliet  84
Berlin  69, 70, 84, 85, 92, 93
Beveridge  32
Bilstein (Crane)  70
Blitz (krieg)  24, 26
Boer War  2
Bofors (Gun)  42
Boulton and Paul  51, 52
Bovington  5, 12, 14, 22
Bren Gun Carrier  12, 31
Brimec  85, 96
British Army of the Rhine (BAOR)  64, 70, 75, 78, 81, 95
British Expeditionary Force (BEF)  3, 24, 25
British Liberation Army (BLA)  54
Brontosaurus (Tractor)  72
Browning Machine-Gun  82
Budleigh Salterton  53
Buffalo (Amphibian)  46, 79
Buntingford  53
Burford  14
Burrows  6
Butler  5

C47 (Aircraft)  42
Canadian Defence Department  25
Canadian Military Pattern (CMP)  25, 26, 31, 35, 36, 43, 44, 46, 59, 60
Carden (Loyd) (Tank and Carrier)  12, 21
casting  81, 87

Caterpillar (Tractor)  29, 53, 74
Cavalier (Tank)  41, 47
Centaur (Tank)  41, 47
Centurion (Tank)  51, 65, 67, 70, 71, 72, 74, 75, 76, 77, 78, 79, 80, 83, 87, 88
Challenger (Tank)  88
Chamberlain  24
Champ (Truck)  70
Checker Cab  34
Chelsea  19
Chertsey  32, 64, 65, 96
Chevrolet  25, 29, 35, 60
Chieftain (Tank)  65, 76, 81, 83, 87, 88
Chindwin  59
Chinese Civil War  14
Chinook (Helicopter)  89
Christie  13
Churchill (tank)  26, 33, 34, 36, 40, 41, 43, 46, 47, 49, 51, 52, 53, 57, 74, 75, 77, 89
Civilian (CL) (vehicle classification)  65, 87, 93
Civil Defence  13
Coast Artillery  13
Cold War  64, 81
Combat (CT) (vehicle classification)  65, 67, 68, 70, 72, 81, 87
Combat Engineer Tractor  96
Combat Vehicle Reconnaissance (Tracked) (CVR(T))  89
combined operations  54
Combined Operations Experimental Establishment (COXE)  53
Comet (tank)  47, 51
Commander (transporter)  95
Commer  67, 68
Commonwealth Base Workshop  75
Commonwealth Division  74
completely knocked down (CKD)  59
Confrontation  81
Conqueror (tank)  70, 71, 72, 76, 77, 78, 79
Constructor (tractor)  72, 73, 85, 94, 95, 96
Contractor (tractor)  95, 96
Contractor Explorer (recovery vehicle)  95
Corporal (missile)  84
Courtburn  96
Covenanter (tank)  47
Cranes (of Dereham)  21, 25, 33, 34, 38, 50, 51, 52, 58, 59, 70, 72
Crane Fruehauf  95, 96
Craven Tasker  96
Crellin  43
Crimean War  2
crock trains  38
Crofts  49

Cromwell (tank)   41, 47, 51, 57, 88
Crossley   15
Cruiser (tank classification)   13, 76
Crusader (tank)   27, 41, 47, 52
Crusader (tractor)   93, 94, 95, 96
Cugnot   2
Cummins   37

D 7 (tractor)   29, 53
D 8 (tractor)   29, 30, 43, 49, 50, 53, 54, 57, 74
D Day   53, 54
Daimler   79
Dakota (aircraft)   42
de Gaulle   39
Demountable Rack Offloading and Pick Up System (DROPS)   96
Dennis   72
Department of Tank Design and Experiment (DTD&E)   10
depot workshop   7
Desert Rats   27
Diamond T   34, 35, 36, 37, 42, 43, 44, 45, 46, 50, 51, 52, 56, 57, 58, 60, 70, 71, 74
diesel   17, 18, 33, 34, 37, 53, 68, 70, 72, 73, 81, 82, 83, 84, 85, 86, 88, 94, 95
Director of Mechanical Maintenance (DMM)   41
Director of Mechanical Engineering (DME)   35, 41
Director of Mechanisation   10
Director of Munitions Production   11
Director of Ordnance Services (DOS)   29
Director of Ordnance Services (Engineering) (DOS(E))   25
Director of Supplies and Transport (DST)   2
Dodge   35, 60
Dragon (tractor)   20
Dragon Wagon (transporter)   51
dummy axle   6, 15, 18, 70, 73, 85, 86, 96
Dunkirk   25, 26, 30, 41, 52
Duplex Drive (DD) (amphibious tank propulsion system)   54
Dyson   34, 51, 57, 70, 72, 85

Eagle (engine)   94, 96
Eagle Engineering Company   22
Eisenhower   54
Eka   86, 92, 93, 94, 95
El Alamein   39, 41
Elliot and Garood   50
Erhardt   13
Experimental Beach Recovery Section (EBRS)   41, 53
Experimental Recovery Section (ERS)   41, 42, 43, 47, 49, 50, 51, 53, 56, 65, 74
Explorer (recovery vehicle)   66, 67, 69, 72, 73, 84, 93, 94, 95

FV 100   89
FV 106   89
FV 200   70, 71, 77
FV 209   77
FV 214   70, 77
FV 219   77
FV 222   77
FV 300   78

FV 306   78
FV 400   72
FV 430   72, 82
FV 432   72, 82, 89, 96
FV 434   76, 88, 89
FV 500   79, 89
FV 503   79
FV 600   72, 89
FV 1000   71, 72, 73
FV 1001   71
FV 1003   70, 71
FV 1004   71
FV 1119   68
FV 1200   72, 73
FV 1201   72
FV 2691   96
FV 3001   71, 72
FV 3005   71
FV 3011   71
FV 3221   72
FV 3242   95
FV 3301   70, 71
FV 3541   73
FV 3561   86
FV 3601   70, 72
FV 4006   76
FV 4201   87
FV 4204   87
FV 11044   84
FV 11301   66
FV 12001   71
FV 12002   71
FV 12004   85
FV 12006   85
FV 13105   73
FV 13115   68
FV 13218   67
Falaise   55
Fantail (amphibian)   46, 79
Farnborough   12, 17
Federal   37, 42, 44
Fellows   28
Feltham   12
Ferret (scout car)   78, 82
Fighting Vehicle Design Establishment (FVDE)   64, 71
Fighting Vehicle Proving Establishment (FVPE)   32, 42, 51, 64
Fighting Vehicle Research and Development Establishment (FVRDE)   64, 65, 71, 72, 79, 87, 89, 95
First Aid Lorry   6
First Lord of the Admiralty   4, 24
Fitter (MT) Recovery (FMR)   vi
Florida   46
Foden   94, 95, 96
Ford   25, 28, 29, 31, 35, 36, 39, 53, 60
Fording Trials Branch REME   79, 92
Fosters   4
Four Wheel Drive (FWD)   7, 16, 18, 29, 42
Fruehauf   33, 34, 51
Fuller   12

gantry   15, 25, 28, 29, 35, 36, 42, 55, 60, 65, 67, 68
Gardner   18, 33
Garner Motors Ltd   22

Gar Wood   29, 35, 36, 42, 43, 60
General Motors (GMC)   25, 26, 31, 53
general service (GS)   3, 65, 67, 71, 87, 91
General Strike   19
Gibraltar   39
GKN (Sankey)   71, 89
GOLDFLAKE   43
Goodyear Tyre Co   14
Grant (tank)   32, 41, 46, 47
ground anchor   47
Guildford   72
gun carrier   7
gun (artillery) tractor   6, 7, 10, 16, 17, 18, 19, 22, 28, 38, 44, 46, 66, 67, 68, 70, 85, 92
Guy (Motors)   15, 20, 36

Hagglunds   83
half track   7, 10, 14, 17, 29, 30, 38, 57, 76
Hall Scott   51
Hamburg   58
Hamilcar   42
Hardy Motors   18
Harland and Wolff (Shipbuilders)   26
Harvey Frost   59, 85, 96
Hathi (tractor)   13, 14
Hazely Heath   49
Headquarters Middle East Command   30, 36
Heavy Branch Machine Gun Corps (MGC)   4, 5
Herbert Morris   17
Hercules (engine)   34, 70
Hippo (truck model)   21
Hitler   24, 55
Hollebone   41, 42, 47
Holmes   29, 35, 36, 93
Holt (tractor)   4, 7, 19, 29
Honest John (missile)   85
Honey (tank)   32
Hotchkiss (tank)   57
Humber   81, 89
HUSKY   43
Hyster (crane)   36, 37

Indian Army   21, 39, 59
Indian Army Ordnance Corps (IAOC)   59
Indian Electrical and Mechanical Engineers (IEME)   59
infantry combat vehicle   89
infantry tank   13, 26, 27, 76
Instow   53, 79
International   29, 53

Jagd Tiger (tank destroyer)   58
Jaguar   89
Jeep   42, 44, 45, 60, 61
Johnson   10
Joseph Sankey Ltd   71
Joseph Stalin (tank)   77
Junkers Jumo (aircraft engine)   81

K 60 (engine)   82
Karrier   15, 73
Kegresse   14
Kings African Rifles (KAR)   27
King Tiger (tank)   58
Knuckey Truck Co.   51

Korean War  65, 66, 74
Kure  75

L 60 (engine)  65, 81
Lake Commachio  46
Lance (missile)  85
Landing Vehicle Tracked (LVT)  46, 79
Land Rover (latterly Landrover)  69, 70, 82, 85, 92, 96
Landship  4
Laplander (truck model)  92
Leader (truck model)  29
Lee (tank)  32, 45, 49
Lend-Lease  32, 33, 36, 39, 41, 50, 53, 57, 59, 64
Leyland  2, 6, 15, 21, 22, 28, 29, 60, 68, 69, 70, 72, 81, 83, 84, 93, 94, 95
Liddell-Hart  12
Life Guards  79
Light Aid Detachment (LAD)  vi, 11, 27, 28, 55, 64, 74, 79, 82
lines of communication (L of C)  14, 27, 29, 39

M1 (wrecker)  36
M1A1 (wrecker)  56
M3 (tank)  32, 33, 37, 45, 49, 61
M4 (tank)  36, 37, 50, 53
M5 (tank)  74
M6 (tank)  50, 52
M7 (recovery gear)  31
M9 (trailer)  35
M15 (semi-trailer)  51
M19 (transporter)  35
M20 (tractor)  35
M25 (transporter)  51
M26 (tractor)  51
M26A1 (tractor)  51
M31 (tank recovery vehicle)  45, 46, 49, 50
M32 (tank recovery vehicle)  46, 49, 50, 73
M48 (tank)  89
M107 (self propelled gun)  82, 83
M246 (wrecker)  85
M578 (tracked recovery vehicle)  82, 83
machine-gun carrier  18
Machine Gun Corps (MGC)  4
Mack  25, 30, 31, 34, 35, 42, 43, 44, 57, 60, 61, 68
Maginot Line  24
Magirus Deutz  84, 85
Maintenance Techniques Development Establishment (MTDE)  65
MARKET GARDEN  55
Marmon Herrington  29, 31
Martel  21
Master General of Ordnance (MGO)  10, 11
Matador (truck model)  18, 28, 29, 35, 36, 84
Matilda (tank)  13, 18, 24, 26, 52
Meadows  66, 72
Mechanical Transport Advisory Board  10, 14
Mechanical Transport Committee  2
Mechanical Warfare Experimental Establishment (MWEE)  12, 17, 46
Mechanisation Experimental Establishment (MEE)  32, 34

Medium A (tank)  12
Medium C (tank)  12, 19, 22
Medium D (tank)  10, 12
Medium Dragon (tractor)  22
Medium Mark III (tank)  13, 22
Mercedes (Benz)  69, 70, 84
Merrit  13
Mersa Matruh  30
Meteor (engine)  41, 51, 71, 75, 77, 81, 88
Meteorite (engine)  71, 72, 85
Militant (truck model)  84
Military Vehicle Engineering Establishment (MVEE)  84, 87, 95, 96
Ministry of Defence (MOD)  87, 89, 93, 95
Ministry of Labour  32
Ministry of Munitions  4, 10
Ministry of Supply (MOS)  11, 22, 31, 32, 33, 34, 36, 41, 42, 49, 50, 51, 53, 64, 69, 70, 71, 72, 74, 75, 85
mobile division  26
Montgomery  35, 54
Morris (Commercial)  13, 14, 15, 16, 25, 29, 42, 44, 46, 59
Multiwheeler  96
Munich  11, 22, 24

Naples  43, 46
National Service  81
Naval Division  4
Naval Land Equipment  52
Nellie (trench digger)  51
Neptune (amphibian)  79
Normandy  53, 54, 55, 58
North Atlantic Treaty Organisation (NATO)  69, 83, 87
North West Frontier  22, 59

Octopus (truck model)  22
ordnance (mobile) workshop  20, 27
Ottaviana  46
OVERLORD  54

P Company RASC  11, 12, 13
Pacific (Car and Foundry Co)  51, 70, 94
Panther (tank)  76
Panzer IV (tank)  57
Peerless  61
Perkins  94
Persia and Iraq Force (PAIFORCE)  39
Petain  25
Pickfords  34
Pioneer (truck model)  17, 18, 20, 21, 41, 52, 55, 59, 66, 67, 72, 73, 84, 85, 93
Plummett  95
Pointer Willamette  34
Porpoise  53
power pack  88
prisoner of war (POW)  39, 46
Pusan  74

Quartermaster General (QMG)  10

radar  13
Ram (tank)  47, 48, 49, 74
Range Rover  92
Rangoon  59
Ransomes and Rapier  22
Rarden (gun)  89

reactor  84
Reading  41
Recovery and Armoured Fighting Vehicle Repair Training Centre  41, 42
recovery mechanic  vi, 76, 93
Reichsbahn  58
Republic of Korea (ROK)  74
Retriever (truck model)  29
(Reynolds) Boughton  91, 95, 96
Richards  29
Roadless (Traction)  14, 52
Rogers (Brothers)  33, 34, 35, 51, 57
Rolls Royce  13, 65, 68, 70, 72, 73, 76, 81, 85, 88, 94, 95, 96
Rome  46
Rommel  27, 39
Roosevelt  32
Rotinoff  72
Rotzler  89, 94, 95
Rouen  4
Rover  71, 92
Royal Air Force (RAF)  2, 14, 18, 27, 39, 42, 66, 84
Royal Armament Research and Development Establishment (RARDE)  88, 96
Royal Armoured Corps (RAC)  vi, 10, 37, 42, 81, 83
Royal Army Ordnance Corps (RAOC)  10, 11, 12, 15, 16, 20, 21, 22, 25, 27, 28, 29, 31, 32, 35, 37, 41, 46, 47
Royal Army Ordnance Corps (Engineering Branch) (RAOC(E))  vi, 11, 16, 28, 29
Royal Army Service Corps (RASC)  vi, 10, 11, 13, 15, 16, 19, 25, 27, 28, 31, 35, 37, 42, 56, 59, 60, 64, 71, 73, 80
Royal Arsenal  10
Royal Artillery (RA)  11, 73, 74, 82, 83
Royal Australian Electrical and Mechanical Engineers (RAEME)  69, 75, 76
Royal Canadian Ordnance Corps (RCOC)  47
Royal Corps of Transport (RCT)  85, 95
Royal Electrical and Mechanical Engineers (REME)  vi, 27, 32, 35, 37, 38, 39, 40, 41, 42, 43, 46, 47, 52, 53, 54, 55, 57, 59, 61, 64, 65, 66, 67, 68, 70, 73, 75, 79, 80, 81, 83, 85, 88, 89, 92, 93, 94, 95, 96
REME Museum  20, 28, 37, 75, 78, 82, 84
REME Technical Group  82
Royal Engineers (RE)  2, 5, 10, 29, 53, 67, 71, 72, 73, 95, 96
Royal Flying Corps (RFC)  2
Royal Horse Guards  82
Royal Indian Army Service Corps (RIASC)  59, 61
Royal Marines (RM)  53, 80
Royal Naval Air Service (RNAS)  4
Royal New Zealand Electrical and Mechanical Engineers (RNZEME)  67, 68
Royal Ordnance Factory (ROF)  79, 86, 87
Royal Tank Corps (RTC)  10, 12, 22
Royal Tank Regiment (RTR)  4
Rubery Owen  72, 96
Ruston and Hornsby  7

S24 (truck model)  95, 96
S26 (truck model)  95, 96
SP 70 (self propelled gun)  89, 94

Saladin (armoured car)   72, 78, 79, 89
Salerno   43
salvage   7, 8, 47
salvage lorry   6, 7, 8
Sampson (armoured recovery vehicle)   89, 90
Saracen (armoured personnel carrier)   72, 78, 79, 84, 89
Saxon (armoured personnel carrier)   89
Scammell   17, 18, 19, 20, 21, 22, 25, 26, 30, 33, 34, 35, 37, 39, 41, 43, 44, 50, 51, 52, 54, 55, 56, 59, 61, 66, 67, 68, 69, 72, 73, 74, 83, 84, 85, 93, 94, 95
Scheldt   54, 55
School of Electrical and Mechanical Engineering (SEME)   65, 87, 95
School of Tank Technology   52
Scimitar (tank)   89
Scorpion (tank)   89
SEALION   26
Self Contained Underwater Breathing Apparatus (SCUBA)   53
Shanghai   14
sheerlegs   7, 8
Shelvoke and Drewry   34, 50, 51
Sherman (tank)   36, 40, 41, 45, 46, 47, 48, 49, 50, 53, 54, 57, 74, 79
Shoeburyness   78
Siegfried Line   51
Slough   16
Singapore   38, 59, 82
Snomobile (over-snow vehicle)   80, 83
Somua   57
South East Asia Command (SEAC)   59
Southern Command   20
South Mediterranean Oil Co   29
Spartan (armoured personnel carrier)   89
spuds   7
staff cars   7, 96
Stalwart (amphibian)   84, 87
Stockholm   93
Straits of Messina   43
Stuart (tank)   32, 37, 74
Studebaker   61
Stug III (self propelled gun)   57
subsidy scheme   2, 14
Sudan Defence Force   27
(Suez) Canal Zone   25, 26, 27, 29, 30, 34, 37, 39, 44
Super Atlantic (tractor model)   72
Superintendent of Design   10

T2 (tank recovery vehicle)   46, 49
TD 18 (tractor)   29, 53
Tank Corps   vi, 5, 8, 12
Tank Corps Central Workshop   5
tankette   12
Tank Museum   52
Tank Repair and Recovery Committee   25, 41
(tank) transporter   17, 18, 19, 20, 21, 25, 26, 28, 30, 31, 33, 34, 35, 37, 38, 39, 40, 41, 42, 44, 45, 47, 50, 51, 52, 56, 61, 66, 70, 71, 72, 73, 80, 85, 91, 95
(tank) tug   8, 37, 74, 75, 76, 79
Taskers   21, 25, 71, 73
Templin   14
Ten Year Rule   12

Territorial Army (TA)   8, 12, 25, 64, 66, 67, 74, 81, 83, 84
Territorial and Army Volunteer Reserve (T & AVR)   81
Terex   96
Thornton   35
Thornycroft   13, 15, 67, 71, 72, 73, 85, 86, 95
Tiger (tank)   58
Tobruk   28, 38
TORCH   39, 41
Tortoise (self propelled gun)   50, 70,
Treasury   12, 64
Turner   85, 94, 95

unditching beam   7
United Nations (UN)   68, 74
United States Army Air Force (USAAF)   42
United States Ordnance Department   50, 84
Universal Carrier   12
Uranus (truck model)   84

Valentine (tank)   26, 27
Vauxhall Motors   26, 67
Vichy   25, 27, 31, 38, 39
Vickers (Armstrong)   12, 13, 19, 21, 76, 83
Vickers Defence Systems   88, 89
Vickers Light Tank   22, 27, 60
Vickers Medium Tank   12, 13, 18, 19, 20, 21, 22
Victory (against) Japan Day (VJ Day)   74
Vijayanta (tank)   83
Volvo   83, 92, 93

War Department (WD)   2, 3, 4, 14, 67, 68, 93
Ward La France   34, 36, 56, 60, 68
Warrior (armoured infantry vehicle)   89
Watford   66, 94
Weaver Manufacturing and Engineering Co   15, 28, 59
Weekes   96
Western Desert Force   26, 30
Western Star   93
Weymouth   53
wheel-cum-track   18
Wheeled Vehicle Experimental Establishment (WVEE)   32, 42, 50, 64, 65
White   25, 30, 31, 34
Whiteley   37
White-Ruxtall   30
Wilson   13
winch   2, 6, 15, 16, 17, 18, 21, 22, 26, 28, 33, 35, 36, 37, 39, 40, 42, 46, 47, 49, 50, 51, 52, 53, 54, 56, 57, 61, 66, 68, 69, 70, 71, 73, 74, 75, 76, 77, 79, 82, 83, 84, 85, 86, 87, 89, 91, 92, 93, 94, 96
Winston Churchill   4, 24, 51
Winter Weiss   34
wrecker   29, 35, 36, 43, 56, 70, 93

ZIPPER   59, 60

1st Armoured Division   25
1st Army   39
2-pounder gun   13
3rd Hussars   28
4 Base Workshop   28, 39
4th Royal Tank Regiment   82
5 Command Workshop   53
5th US Army   43
6-pounder gun   4, 5, 41
7th Armoured Division   26, 27
7 Armoured Workshop   76
8-inch howitzer   83
8th Army   26, 29, 33, 39, 43
8th Army Recovery Company   27, 37
10 Base Workshop   61
13 Command Workshop   49, 75
17-pounder gun   88
19 Tank Transporter Company   71
21st Army Group   43, 53, 54, 56
22 Advanced Base Workshop   56, 57
25 Beach Recovery Section
25th Tank Brigade   40
27th Armoured Brigade   54
27 Command Workshop   73, 76
30mm gun   89
37mm gun   33
38 Central Workshop   85, 88
47mm gun   12
69 Infantry Brigade Workshop   29
75mm gun   33, 40, 41
76mm gun   78, 89
79th Armoured Division   46
81mm mortar   50
93 MT Company   6
105mm gun   76, 83, 92
120mm gun   77
670 Army Recovery Company   43
686 Infantry Troops Workshop   46
711 MT Company   5
835 Heavy Recovery Section   57, 58

Printed in the United Kingdom for
Her Majesty's Stationery Office
Dd 238644 C30 1/89 54135